# YOU RIGHTS

## TO HEALTH CARE

LORNA EASTERBROOK

**Published by Age Concern England**
1268 London Road
London SW16 4ER

© 2005 Age Concern England

First published 2005

Editor Gillian Clarke
Production Leonie Farmer
Cover design Vincent McEvoy
Typeset by GreenGate Publishing Services, Tonbridge, Kent
Printed in Great Britain by Bell & Bain Ltd, Glasgow

A catalogue record for this book is available from the British Library.

ISBN-13: 978-0-86242-398-8
ISBN-10: 0-86242-398-8

# CONTENTS

Acknowledgements iv
About the author v
Introduction vi
1. 'I know my rights' 1
2. Asking for and getting help 24
3. GPs and primary care services 34
4. Dentistry 48
5. Eye services 61
6. Hearing services 71
7. Therapists, and other support 79
8. Mental health 102
9. Chiropody and foot care 132
10. Pharmacy 141
11. Going to hospital 150
12. Coming out of hospital 168
13. NHS care where you live 178
14. Organ and blood donation 197
15. Death and dying 205
16. Making complaints 223
17. Information and communication 247
18. Getting involved in the NHS 256
19. Keeping up to date with change 262
Appendix: Useful addresses 264
About Age Concern 285
Publications from Age Concern Books 286
Index 290

# ACKNOWLEDGEMENTS

A number of people have been involved in the production of this book, whether with layout, editing, comments or general support. Thanks must go to staff at Age Concern England – particularly Leonie Farmer, who good-naturedly kept everyone on track and to time; to the library staff, who kindly shared their work space on many occasions; and to Pauline Thompson and Philip Hurst in the Policy Unit who, together with Sheelagh Donovan from the Information Department, provided essential comments on draft versions of this book.

Despite this incredibly helpful input, ultimate responsibility for factual accuracy must lie with me.

Acknowledgements can be an odd thing. They can sound overly gushing and contrived ('finally, I must also thank the postman, for delivering the manuscript'); consist of slightly bizarre entries ('thanks also to Binky and Tiny, for tea, biscuits and tail wagging'); or just list the many people to whom the author has probably forgotten to send a birthday card in the past year. That aside, this book was helped hugely by the editorial skills, kindness and patience of Gillian Clarke; by the ability of my friends and mum to tolerate (and support) my disappearance for large amounts of time; and can only be dedicated to The Cat, who is ever-hopeful that we will play in the garden for as long as he would like.

# ABOUT THE AUTHOR

**Lorna Easterbrook** began working with and for older people as a theatre stage manager taking productions into older people's care homes, long-stay hospital wards and other community settings. She then spent ten years working in the voluntary sector, for a Care and Repair Home Improvement Agency; Age Concern England; and the King's Fund, where she was Fellow in Community Care.

Since 2000 she has worked as an independent consultant, specialising in issues in health, housing and social care services for older people, including work for national telephone helpline services answering queries about health, care and support from older people, their families and friends.

Aside from her stint training for the theatre (Royal Welsh College of Music and Drama), Lorna has degrees in Archaeology and Prehistory (University of Sheffield) and Social Policy and Planning (London School of Economics).

# INTRODUCTION

This book provides information about the main entitlements to health care for older people, particularly NHS services provided in England. All of the information applies to people aged 60 and over but much of the detail also applies to younger adults.

*Your Rights to Health Care* covers all types of health care and health needs, from chiropody and toenail cutting to dentistry, major operations and long-term care. Although many of the subjects covered are complicated, this book aims to explain them in as clear and straightforward a way as possible. It cannot cover all situations and circumstances, so each chapter indicates how to find out more information, including details of Age Concern Factsheets and other local and national sources of help.

Much of the treatment you receive as an individual depends on the precise nature of your illness or disability. So this book cannot diagnose what might be wrong with you or tell you whether you are receiving the right type of the medication; but it can tell you about getting a diagnosis and what to do if you are worried about your medicines. It also explains your rights if you find that you need health care.

## Where you live in the United Kingdom

All the information applies to people living in England, although some will also be relevant throughout the UK. For further information specifically about health care in Scotland, Wales or Northern Ireland, contact Age Concern Scotland, Age Concern Cymru or Age Concern Northern Ireland. Their addresses are on page 285.

*Your Rights to Health Care* also includes some information for people who used to live in England but now live abroad, outlining their entitlement to health care from the NHS on their visits back to England.

# Keeping up to date

This book is based on information available in February 2005. As in the past, though, arrangements for health care might well change in the future. For example, in the 1980s older people lost their right to free eyesight tests, only for this right to be reinstated in 1999. Some rights have existed for only a few years whereas others have been in place for over 50 years. Chapter 1 explains some of the ways these changes happen, and a number of possible future changes are mentioned throughout the book.

Chapter 19 gives you some ideas on keeping up to date with change. If you need information on the latest position on these issues, or you have questions about particular points, please write to Age Concern at the address given on page 285. You might also like to contact NHS Direct (details on page 279).

# How to use this book

One of the aims of this book is to provide a jargon-free explanation of your rights to health care. But we have deliberately included some terms and phrases because you are likely to come across them at some point as they are commonly used in the NHS. Box 1 gives some examples.

Different types of health care and health care services are described in separate chapters. You can dip in and out of this book or read it as a whole. If you want to know where and how your rights to the NHS are set out, you could start with Chapter 1. But if you only want to know about your rights to NHS eyesight services (for example), you could just read about this in Chapter 5. The index should also help you to find the relevant information.

Contact details of all the organisations mentioned in this book are given in the Appendix.

## Box 1 Examples of terms

**Carers** In this book 'carer' means someone who provides support to another person (whether through practical help or personal care or with emotional support) but isn't paid to do this. This might be a member of your family, a friend or a neighbour ... or you. Sometimes, carers are also called 'family carers', 'informal carers' or even 'unpaid carers'.

**Integrated services** These are provided together (jointly) by social services departments and the NHS. Examples include Falls Clinics (to help reduce the numbers of falls by older people) and Joint Equipment Stores.

**Local council** or **local authority** This is the system of local government where you live – the London or Metropolitan Borough, County Council or Unitary Authority. Social services and housing departments are part of the local authority/local council.

**Multi-disciplinary** This term describes the different profession-als who may work together to support your health needs – for example, the doctor, physiotherapist, social worker and nurse.

**Private organisations** There are many different private health clinics and hospitals, some of which may have a contract with the NHS to provide care for NHS patients. Some health professionals have private patients as well as working in the NHS.

**Voluntary organisations** These include charities and not-for-profit organisations such as housing associations. Voluntary organisations can consist of paid staff as well as volunteers.

# Chapter 1

# 'I know my rights'

Most of us know that we have rights and entitlements, but we may not always know what they are in practice. This chapter explores the rights we have to NHS services in England. To begin with, though, it may be helpful to set out briefly how the NHS works.

## How does the NHS work?

The NHS is quite complicated. It consists of lots of different organisations, all with their own role and responsibilities. In broad terms the NHS consists of:

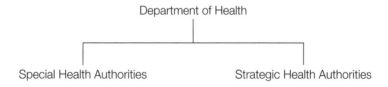

Department of Health

Special Health Authorities          Strategic Health Authorities

## Department of Health (DH)

Civil servants at the Department of Health work with the Secretary of State for Health and others to draw up and issue laws, regulations, guidance and targets.

## Special Health Authorities (SHAs)

Some cover the whole of the UK, such as UK Transplant; others, such as the Health Protection Agency, cover only England and Wales. Other examples of Special Health Authorities include NHS Direct, the National Institute for Health and Clinical Excellence and the National Blood Service.

## Strategic Health Authorities (StHAs)

There are 28 Strategic Health Authorities in England. They develop plans for improving health services in their areas, and monitor the performance of local health services. They support Primary Care Trusts and NHS Trusts in putting national policies into practice.

**Primary Care Trusts (PCTs)** England is subdivided into a large number of local areas, with a Primary Care Trust responsible for managing NHS services in each area. Primary Care Trusts provide community services such as district nursing; and they contract (or commission) other services that they must ensure are available from the NHS in their area. The services they are responsible for include GPs, dentists, opticians, mental health services, hospital services, NHS Walk-In Centres, transport for patients (including accident and emergency), screening and pharmacies. Primary Care Trusts must make sure there are enough health services in their area – including planning for the future. They also have to ensure that the local health and social care systems are working together to improve things for patients. Since April 2005, GP practices have been able to choose to commission (purchase) some NHS services for their patients (see Chapter 3).

**NHS Trusts** manage a range of NHS services; each organisation is managed by a separate NHS Trust. Some NHS Trusts are regional or national centres for more specialised care. Others work with particular universities to help train health professionals. The most commonly known Trusts are local NHS hospitals. Trusts can also provide services in the community; for example, through health centres or clinics.

Other important organisations are:

- **Foundation Trusts** are a more recent type of NHS hospital/organisation run by local managers, staff and members of the public. Foundation status only began in April 2004 so there are not many of these so far.
- **Mental Health Trusts** provide specialist NHS mental health services, such as hospital places and community support for people with severe mental health problems. They may also offer some therapy and specialist medical help.
- **Ambulance Trusts** – there are 38 of these in England, providing emergency access to health care. They may also provide non-emergency transport if they have a contract with the local Primary Care Trust to do so.
- **Care Trusts** provide both health and social care. There are only a few of these at present, and they tend to provide specific services such as mental health or care for older people.

## Where are our rights set out?

People who believe they have a particular right to something often think this must be set out in law. Yet there is no 'Magna Carta' for the NHS. In other words, there's no single document or Act of Parliament that sets out *every* individual's entitlement to *all* NHS services. Instead, our rights to health care come from many different sources, many of which have changed over time (and keep changing). These include:

- Acts of Parliament (also called statutes).
- Case law – when individuals have challenged the NHS by taking

a legal case to the High Court and established a new understanding of what the NHS must do.

■ Directions, Regulations and Guidance. These are issued by governments to describe the detail of how particular sections (or clauses) in Acts of Parliament should be put into practice.

■ Best practice – there are three general types of best practice. The first is what is generally accepted at the time by health care professionals and health organisations as the best way of providing treatment or care. The second type is how government uses examples to support a particular approach, such as services that help reduce the numbers of older people who fall. The third is 'evidence-based' best practice – for example, the National Institute for Health and Clinical Excellence (NICE) looks at all the available clinical evidence on particular drugs, operations or other treatments, before telling the NHS what it should (and should not) be offering to patients.

■ Standards of services – which can cover the buildings where services are provided as well as the behaviour of staff and the treatment received.

■ Government policy decisions. This is when the government of the day decides it will introduce a change to the NHS that doesn't require a new law to be passed.

## Acts of Parliament

Although some people may believe that our rights to the NHS are all described in great detail in Acts of Parliament, this is not the case. But Acts of Parliament do play a crucial role. The NHS itself would not exist, for example, without the original National Health Service Act of 1946 (much of which has since been replaced by later Acts).

Acts of Parliament relating to health tend to set out the key or major ways in which health services and organisations are to be provided, funded and run in this country. They are sometimes called 'primary legislation'. Regulations are then issued by Parliament to explain more of the detail of the law – these are sometimes called 'secondary legislation' (see page 9); the Secretary of State for Health also issues Directions and Guidance, which often go into further detail about applying the law in practice.

The most important right that we all share, and which *is* set out in an Act, is that the Secretary of State for Health (whoever she or he is at the time) has a duty to make sure that the NHS provides what is judged to be needed for the whole population, within available resources. This is in the NHS Act of 1977.

But providing sufficient services across the population isn't the same as every single person having the right *no matter what* to receive a particular treatment. We don't all have this right, partly because we are unlikely all to need the same treatment. Another reason is that the NHS doesn't provide every possible treatment – some plastic surgery, for example, is not available on the NHS.

An example of something the NHS *does* provide is treatment for cancer. Because we will not all develop cancer (although many will and do), it would make no sense for all of us to have an individual right to receive treatment for cancer because this would mean that people without cancer would be just as entitled to demand – and get – treatment they didn't need.

Nevertheless, the Secretary of State has a duty to make sure that *enough* cancer treatment is provided for everyone in the population who *does* get this disease *at the time it develops in their life*. This means that, if at any stage in my life I develop cancer, I have a right to expect that the NHS will provide the treatment NHS doctors say I need. I have this right because the NHS must provide the services that the Secretary of State for Health says are needed across the population, of whom I am one person, and which include cancer care. So my right to NHS care comes when I actually need the sort of treatment that the NHS has been told should be available to help me.

The Secretary of State doesn't reach a judgement about the services that are needed on his or her own. It is only that he or she has the legal *duty* to make sure the NHS provides enough treatment within available resources. This is important in terms of the amount of funding received by the NHS as well as how the funding is spent.

---

### Box 2. 'Enough treatment'

You may be surprised at the idea of 'enough treatment', especially if you (or someone you know) feel you have not received 'enough' treatment from the NHS, needed because of a particular illness, disease or disability. But this is where your 'rights' to health care are also closely linked with the clinical judgement of the health professionals treating you. They play a very important role in deciding what sorts of treatment or support you should receive, for how long, and why.

Which means that this book cannot tell everyone who has a stroke (for example) exactly what medication they will be given, or exactly how long they might stay in hospital, or whether the NHS will definitely fund their longer-term care. These are matters of clinical judgement that will vary according to each person's circumstances. But it does explain the overall rights to health care shared by everyone who has a stroke, no matter their individual circumstances.

---

Most Acts tend to set out how the NHS and other providers of health services should be structured, regulated and inspected, and how health care professionals should be registered and patients protected.

In recent years there has been a lot of new legislation that affects how health care is funded, regulated and provided. If you are interested in finding out more about relevant Acts of Parliament, you can:

■ see if there are copies you can read in the Reference section of your local library;

■ search on the Internet – for example, on the website for the House of Commons (www.parliament.uk/commons), or The Stationery Office, which publishes Acts of Parliament and other official documents (www.hmso.gov.uk);

■ ask your MP for information about recent Acts;

■ find books that look at these aspects in more detail, such as the annual *Welfare Rights Handbook* published by the Child Poverty Action Group (CPAG; contact details on page 268). Your local library may have a copy of this book.

A number of charities also provide information about the NHS, including explaining what the law says should happen. Some charities, such as Age Concern England and Help the Aged, have details for any older person. Others, such as the Alzheimer's Society, the Parkinson's Disease Society and Arthritis Care, have information aimed at people with those particular health conditions, and their families and friends. Details of these charities and other useful organisations are given in the Appendix.

## Case law

Case law describes the ruling when an individual takes a case to the High Court (or to a higher court, such as the Court of Appeal). This involves the person testing out some aspect of the law, to see how it applies in his or her circumstances. Often, they bring a case to court because they feel they have grounds to challenge a decision that the NHS has made about their care.

There are lots of challenges and case law that are quite well known. They include:

- **The case involving Tony Bland** Mr Bland was left in a 'persistent vegetative state' (PVS) after being involved in the disaster at Hillsborough football ground, Sheffield, in 1989. His parents sought the court's help to decide whether or not doctors could lawfully withdraw the artificially provided food and fluid he was receiving.

- **The case of Diane Blood** Mrs Blood's husband died very unexpectedly and quickly. At her request, and in line with what he had previously told her he would want to happen in these circumstances, his sperm was taken and frozen after his death by health professionals. But because her husband's views were not written down, Mrs Blood had to go to court to get permission to use it in her fertility treatment to try to conceive the children she and her husband had planned.

- **The case of Diane Pretty** Mrs Pretty had motor neurone disease (MND), a gradual disease for which there is no cure at present. The effect of the disease meant that as she reached the end of her life it was very unlikely she would be able to commit suicide unaided. She wanted to know that, if it was her clear wish that her husband assist her, he would not be prosecuted afterwards if he had helped.

- **The case of 'Miss B'** Miss B was a social worker who was profoundly injured in an accident. She went to court to prove she was mentally capable of deciding not to continue with artificial support, in the full knowledge that this would hasten her death.

- **The case of 'Child B'** Child B's father went to the courts on behalf of his daughter, who was terminally ill with cancer. He challenged the decision of the NHS doctors and hospital that were responsible for her care not to try any further treatment once a certain stage had been reached. The doctors felt it was not in her interests to continue with treatment that could not prolong her life but that, in their view, might cause her further distress.

■ **The case of Pamela Coughlan** Ms Coughlan's injuries from a road traffic accident were so severe that she lived in a specialist NHS unit; when she had moved there she had been told that it would be her home for life. When the relevant NHS health authority decided to change the sort of service offered by this unit, it said she could not remain in the unit but would have to move to a nursing home and pay towards the cost of this care. She challenged the health authority's decision that it was no longer responsible for funding or providing her care.

If someone (or an organisation) is ruled against, the judge's decision can be challenged; ultimately, the Law Lords (some of the most senior members of the judiciary, who sit in the House of Lords) hear the highest court challenges.

There are many examples of case law apart from those listed above. Doctors, patients, lawyers and others use case law to work out what is lawful according to the current understanding of the law. Many case law rulings, though, are quite specific to the detail of the particular individual who brought the case. This can mean that, later on, another person will bring a case that is similar (but not identical) to a case that has already been heard, because some further clarification is needed.

Case law is often reported in broadsheet newspapers, such as *The Times*. Major cases often feature in the news on TV and radio.

## Directions, Regulations and Guidance

*Regulations* (also called Statutory Instruments) are issued by Parliament. They explain more of the detail of particular Acts of Parliament. *Directions* and *Guidance* are issued by the Secretary of

State for Health and go into more detail about putting these Acts into practice. Unlike Acts of Parliament, Directions, Regulations and Guidance can be changed fairly easily and quickly – provided that whatever is issued stays within the current legal understanding of what the Act says. Recent examples of Directions, Guidance and Regulations include:

- The NHS's contribution to the costs of registered nursing care in care homes (see Chapter 13).
- NHS responsibilities to provide continuing health care for older people and others (see Chapter 13).
- Access to NHS health care for overseas visitors to the UK (see Chapter 13).

Another example is the arrangements for the services provided by general practitioners (GPs) that began on 1 April 2004 (see Chapter 3 for more details about GPs).

## Best practice and standards of service

Lots of different organisations look at various aspects of best practice and standards of service. They may also regulate services according to nationally set standards. They include:

- **The National Institute for Health and Clinical Excellence (NICE)** makes recommendations to the NHS across England and Wales on the treatments (including medicines) and care it should provide. It does this by considering the best available evidence. You have the right to expect the NHS to provide the treatments that NICE recommends.
- **The Healthcare Commission** inspects NHS services in England and Wales such as hospitals and clinics. It also regulates and inspects private and voluntary health care services in England, under the Care Standards Act 2000. And it plays a part in the

NHS complaints system (see Chapter 16). It aims to help improve the quality of these services. You have the right to expect that services inspected or regulated by the Healthcare Commission meet certain minimum standards.

■ **The National Patient Safety Agency (NPSA)** is responsible for how errors and incidents within the NHS are reported. It aims to improve the safety of NHS patients. One example is by issuing guidance to NHS staff on keeping their hands clean. You have the right to bring any errors and other incidents to the attention of the NPSA.

The Government published *Standards for Better Health* in the summer of 2004. This sets out all the targets that the NHS must either meet now or work towards for the future (see also page 18).

It also describes a series of core standards that all NHS services must already meet. This includes services that the NHS buys on behalf of patients from private health clinics or voluntary organisations. The Healthcare Commission reviews all the NHS's services against these core standards. It will also look at each organisation's progress towards a series of developmental standards.

There is more about these standards on page 19.

## Government policy decisions

One example of a government policy decision is NHS eyesight tests. People over the age of 60 used not to have to pay for eyesight tests from the NHS. At the end of the 1980s, however, the government of the day decided to withdraw free eyesight tests for older people. It did this by making an announcement and withdrawing the scheme. No new Act of Parliament was required because there was no Act that said that everyone over the age of 60 was entitled to a free eyesight test.

In 1999, a different government decided it would re-introduce this entitlement. It also announced the change, put in place the necessary arrangements to reimburse optometrists who carried out the tests, and made sure that any government leaflets about having eyesight tests included this information. Again, this change didn't need a new Act of Parliament or even a new Regulation.

Many rights such as the entitlement to free eyesight tests are not necessarily permanent, or set in stone. Our rights may change depending on the government of the day, and current views about how different health care matters should be pursued.

## Targets

Another very good example of government policy creating 'rights' is by its setting targets for how quickly you should be able to see your GP or how soon after being referred you should have an operation or other hospital treatment. There is more about the targets for different types of NHS care in the relevant chapters in this book.

Targets are not universally popular, and in 2004 the number of targets the NHS has to meet were reduced. But while they exist, they give all of us, as NHS patients, a clearer idea of what we have the right to expect. See also page 18.

## **Other rights**

Other rights are universal – we all have them. They are partly set out in the law, partly established by case law, and form part of government policy. They include:

- the right to receive primary care from a GP (see Chapter 3);
- the right to an NHS dentist (see Chapter 4);
- the right to complain about services (see Chapter 16).

We also can expect certain things, such as:

- to have our human rights respected, as set out in the Human Rights Act 1998 (under the European Convention on Human Rights);
- not to be unfairly discriminated against because of our age;
- to receive the NHS treatment we need, regardless of how much (or how little) money we have.

Some of these rights are fundamental to the whole NHS. They are the principles or the starting point for the running of all NHS services. Many have been in place since the NHS began, in 1948. More recently, they have been repeated in documents such as *The NHS Plan* and the various National Service Frameworks (NSFs).

## The NHS Plan and National Service Frameworks

In 2000 the Government published *The NHS Plan*. This set out ten core principles of the NHS (Box 3).

National Service Frameworks (NSFs) set national standards for particular services (eg cancer care or renal services) or a particular part of the population (such as older people), as part of an overall drive to improve services. Each National Service Framework sets out the dates by which any changes should be in place. National Service Frameworks are being published one at a time over a period of some years, beginning in 2001.

For anyone aged 65 or over, the most important one is the National Service Framework for Older People. This sets out eight standards to be met by the NHS (Box 4), together with local authority (local council) social services departments where this is appropriate.

---

**Box 3. The ten principles of the NHS**

The NHS will:

1. Provide a universal service for all, based on clinical need, not ability to pay.
2. Provide a comprehensive range of services.
3. Shape its services around the needs and preferences of individual patients, their families and carers.
4. Respond to the different needs of different populations.
5. Work continuously to improve quality services and to minimise errors.
6. Support and value its staff.
7. Devote public funds for health care solely to NHS patients.
8. Work together with others to ensure a seamless service for patients.
9. Keep people healthy and work to reduce health inequalities.
10. Respect the confidentiality of individual patients and provide open access to information about services, treatment and performance.

---

There has been some confusion as to whether older people only come under the National Service Framework for Older People. But most of the other National Service Frameworks also apply to older people. The exception is the National Service Framework for Mental Health, which is written for adults up to the age of 65 – although, even here, there are some overlaps for the small number of older people whose severe mental health problems began when they were under the age of 65; or who are already 65 but develop a severe psychotic illness. (See also Chapter 8.)

Box 4. The eight standards of the National Service
Framework for Older People

1.  **Rooting out age discrimination** You should not be
    discriminated against (treated unfairly) by the NHS or
    social services because of your age. NHS services should
    be provided on the basis of your clinical need –
    regardless of how old you are. Social services must not
    use age in their eligibility criteria to restrict people's
    access to services.

2.  **Person-centred care** You should be treated as an
    individual, and be able to make choices about your care.
    The NHS and social services should make this possible
    by using the Single Assessment Process (SAP) to assess
    older people's needs for care and support. The NHS and
    social services should together run community equipment
    services and continence services (sometimes this type of
    service is called a 'joint' or 'integrated' service).

3.  **Intermediate care** The NHS and social services should
    provide increasing amounts of intermediate care services
    to help older people stay at home for as long as possible
    and to reduce the number of unnecessary hospital
    admissions (see Chapter 7).

4.  **General hospital care** All NHS hospitals that provide
    care for older patients must have a specialist old-age
    multi-disciplinary team, and have an agreement about
    how older patients' health needs will be looked after
    across different hospital wards, clinics and departments.
    It will be clear to patients who in the hospital has the
    overall responsibility for the nursing care of its older
    patients (eg a matron or other senior nursing staff).

5. **Stroke** All NHS general hospitals that provide care for people who have had a stroke (including younger adults), must have a specialised stroke service. All GPs work to a local agreement for identifying and referring their patients who are at risk of stroke.

6. **Falls** All local health providers (including independent organisations) must have procedures in place to help reduce the risk of older people falling. There should be an integrated falls service (see page 86) in each area by April 2005.

7. **Mental health** The NHS and social services should use the same set of rules to manage older people's mental health. GPs should use a locally agreed procedure to diagnose, refer and treat any patient who has depression or dementia.

8. **The promotion of health and active age in older life** Local plans drawn up by the NHS, social services and others should include programmes that promote good mental health, and make sure that people know about flu vaccinations and other measures.

There are also National Service Frameworks for:

- coronary heart disease (CHD)
- diabetes
- renal services
- cancer.

A further National Service Framework for people with neurological and other long-term conditions is expected during 2005. This will look at NHS care for people with epilepsy, multiple sclerosis (MS),

Parkinson's disease, motor neurone disease (MND), and brain and spinal injuries. It will also look at issues that apply to people with other long-term conditions and disabilities, such as information about services, rehabilitation, and care and support at home.

Under the NSF for Coronary Heart Disease, some of the things you can expect include:

- help to stop smoking;
- advice and treatment if you are identified by your GP as being at significant risk of cardiovascular disease;
- professional assessment if you are thought to be having a heart attack and aspirin given, if indicated, within 60 minutes of asking for professional help from the NHS;
- appropriate advice and treatment if you are admitted to hospital with a heart attack;
- symptoms of angina or suspected angina to be investigated and treatment given to relieve pain and reduce the risk of this becoming more serious;
- referral to a cardiologist as a matter of urgency if your angina becomes more frequent or more severe;
- suspected heart failure to be confirmed (or ruled out) and the reasons identified;
- to be invited to take part in a programme designed to reduce your risk of later problems from coronary heart disease.

Under the NSF for Cancer (often called The Cancer Plan), you can expect:

- to be *invited* for breast screening, if you are a woman aged up to 70 (women over the age of 70 have the right to *ask* for – and receive – breast screening but will not receive an invitation to do so);

- not to wait more than one month from diagnosis to treatment for all cancers;
- to wait no more than two months from your GP making an urgent referral to your being treated by a cancer specialist.

The NSF for Diabetes is in two parts. The first part covers aspects such as:

- receiving good-quality care throughout your lifetime, including support to control your blood glucose and blood pressure;
- being encouraged to take part in decisions about your treatment and care, and supported to lead a healthy life;
- to have your diabetes managed effectively during a stay in hospital for whatever reason.

The second part of the diabetes NSF, looking at issues such as primary care and end-of-life care, is expected during 2005.

## Our rights to the NHS

We all share the same basic rights. These include:

- respect for confidentiality (see Chapter 17);
- respect for our privacy, dignity, and religious and cultural beliefs;
- clean and safe hospitals and clinics;
- free care from our GP, nursing and therapeutic staff (see Chapters 3 and 7);
- free hospital consultant care (see Chapter 11);
- to receive a reasonable standard of care;
- to receive the treatment, medication and equipment necessary for our clinical needs.

*Standards for Better Health* sets out the standards of care that all NHS services should provide. These standards also give us rights as to what we can expect from the NHS. There are seven categories, called 'domains'. Under each domain there are several core standards, which the NHS must be meeting already, and some developmental standards, which the NHS must work towards achieving over the next three to four years (Box 5).

---

**Box 5. Examples of core standards in the seven domains**

1. **Safety** Health care organisations keep patients, staff and visitors safe by having systems to ensure that the risk of health care-acquired infection to patients is reduced, with particular emphasis on high standards of hygiene and cleanliness, achieving year-on-year reductions in MRSA.

2. **Clinical and cost effectiveness** Health care organisations co-operate with each other and with social care organisations to ensure that patients' individual needs are properly managed and met.

3. **Governance** Health care organisations undertake all appropriate employment checks and ensure that all employed or contracted professionally qualified staff are registered with the appropriate bodies; and require that all employed professionals abide by relevant published codes of professional practice.

4. **Patient focus** Health care organisations have systems in place to ensure that staff treat patients and their relatives and carers with dignity and respect; that appropriate consent is obtained when required for all contacts with patients and for the use of any confidential patient information; and that staff treat patient information confidentially, except where authorised by legislation to the contrary.

---

5. **Accessible and responsive care** Health care organisations enable all members of the population to access services equally, and offer choice in access to services and treatment equitably.

6. **Care environment and amenities** Health care services are provided in safe and secure environments that promote effective care and optimise health outcomes and that protect patients, staff, visitors and their property and the physical assets of the organisation; and are supportive of patient privacy and confidentiality.

7. **Public health** Care organisations have systematic and managed disease-prevention and health-promotion programmes that meet the requirements of the National Service Frameworks and national plans with particular regard to reducing obesity through action on nutrition and exercise, smoking, substance misuse and sexually transmitted infections.

*Standards for Better Health* also reminds the NHS of the targets (or commitments) it must be meeting now or working towards achieving in the next two to three years. Details of these targets (or commitments) are included throughout this book in the relevant chapters.

# Rights for older people

All adults have the same basic entitlements to NHS services, but there are some additional rights for older people:

■ Free flu vaccination – each year (usually in the late autumn and early winter). This is available to everyone aged 65 or over. You should receive a letter from your GP's surgery inviting you to come in. But if you don't get a letter, there is nothing to stop you asking for an appointment. And you can refuse the vaccination – it must be available for you but you don't have to accept.

- Free pneumonia vaccination if you are aged 75 or over. From 2005, this will also be available for those aged 65 or over. It aims to protect you against pneumonia, septicaemia and bacterial meningitis.

- You can ask for a free annual health check if you are aged 75 or over, if you have not seen your GP/health professional in the past 12 months. This takes place at your GP's surgery, but might be carried out by a nurse rather than your GP. If you find it hard to visit the practice because of medical reasons, this check can be carried out at home.

- Free medication check if you are 75 or over. This should be carried out every year – and is part of the National Service Framework for Older People. If you are taking four or more different medicines, your check should happen every six months. Your GP, or possibly a local pharmacist (the chemist), may carry this out. You may be given a leaflet, 'Focus on Your Medicines', before the check to help you think about the sorts of questions you might be asked – if you're not given this, ask for a copy.

- Free NHS prescriptions if you are aged 60 or over.
- Free NHS eyesight tests if you are aged 60 or over.

Most NHS services are free. But there are charges for some, such as NHS dentistry, any glasses (spectacles) or contact lenses you may need, wigs and some other type of support such as elastic stockings or corsets. But there is also help with these health costs for people on low incomes – including older people. There is more about this scheme, and about any costs for NHS services, in Chapter 7.

Age Concern Factsheet 44 *NHS services and older people* and Information Sheet IS20 *Help with health costs for older people* also explain about this.

## The NHS's rights

It may come as a bit of a surprise to learn that the NHS also has rights. More specifically, there are certain things that are expected of you by the people who work for NHS organisations.

For example, NHS staff have the right to expect not to be attacked – either physically or verbally. If you assault a member of staff, the NHS is within its rights to:

- Ask you to leave the premises – and escort you out of the door if needed.
- Call the police and press charges against you.

You will often find details about the type of patient behaviour that is unacceptable on posters put up around NHS hospitals, GP surgeries or other clinics. You should also try to treat staff respectfully. This means not behaving in a way that is racist or sexist or causes offence.

If you do offend a member of staff but did not mean to, the best thing to do is apologise and explain that no offence was meant. If you do not understand why a member of staff has taken offence, ask them or one of their colleagues to explain this to you. But even if you have offended a member of NHS staff, they should not retaliate against you in any way.

Recently there has been some discussion about whether patients who fail to turn up for appointments (or who don't let staff know they can't keep the appointment) should be fined a sum of money. So far, this suggestion hasn't been accepted or introduced. Nevertheless, if you cannot get to an appointment, make sure you ring or write to let staff know as soon as you can – and make sure your letter or call reaches them before the appointment is due. This way, they have a chance to offer it to another patient. If an emergency means that you are unable to attend at the last minute, get in touch as soon as you can afterwards to explain this.

## Chapter 2

# Asking for and getting help

There are lots of different ways you can ask for help because of a health worry – whether you think this is something that can wait or you need advice and help as a matter or urgency. They include:

- NHS Direct (NHS Helpline in Scotland);
- NHS Direct Online (the website of NHS Direct);
- GP surgeries and out-of-hours services;
- NHS Walk-In Centres;
- pharmacists;
- hospital Accident & Emergency (A&E) units;
- 999 calls and emergency services;
- Minor Injuries Units.

There are some private medical walk-in facilities, such as the Medi-centres at some of London's larger mainline train stations. Chapter 3 looks in more detail at primary care services such as GP surgeries, district nursing and out-of-hours services. Chapter 10 looks in detail at pharmacists.

## NHS Direct

NHS Direct is a Special Health Authority that provides the same service to everyone living in England and Wales.

NHS Direct offers 'nurse-led' advice and information about health matters over the telephone. It works by your telephoning NHS Direct – in England and Wales, the number is 0845 4647. This is not a free call; you will be charged as if you are making a local telephone call (the cost of your making the call will be added to your telephone or mobile bill as usual). You can ring to find out about:

- what to do if you or someone in your family is feeling ill;
- particular health conditions;
- local health care services, such as the nearest doctor, dentist or late-night pharmacy;
- self-help and support organisations.

The NHS employs everyone who works for NHS Direct. Your can ring at any time, 24 hours a day, all year round. Your telephone call will be recorded, but all the information you give is confidential (see also Chapter 17). If you are asking for details of your nearest dentist or pharmacy, the person answering the call will give you this information; but if you are ringing with a health concern, you will either be put through to a nurse or you will be told that a nurse will ring you back. The nurse you speak to at NHS Direct will ask you about the health matter you are calling about – for example, she or he may ask you to describe any symptoms. They will then advise you on the best course of action – for example, if you are feeling ill with flu-like symptoms they may suggest how to look after yourself at home if this is appropriate (eg stay in bed, drink lots of fluids), or advise you to visit your GP or hospital A&E department if things are more serious. If necessary, they can connect you directly to the ambulance service.

If English is not your first language, when you ring NHS Direct you should make sure to give the English name of the language you need to speak in (eg by saying 'French', or 'Urdu', or 'Welsh', or the name of whichever language it is that you want to speak in). If you stay on the line you should be connected to an interpreter who speaks your language; or you can ask someone who does speak English to ring for you, explain that a translator is needed, and then let you speak to the translator when he or she comes on the line.

---

### Box 6. Textphone enquiries

There is also a textphone number you can use to contact NHS Direct. This is aimed at people who are deaf or hard of hearing or who have speech difficulties. The number to call, 0845 606 4647, is also charged at local rates and is available all the time.

NHS Direct says that textphone calls will be answered as soon as possible, but asks people who contact them on the textphone number to wait if they don't get a reply straightaway.

There is more about NHS help for people with hearing difficulties in Chapter 6.

---

Everyone who contacts NHS Direct for advice about their health will be asked to give their name, address, phone number and the name of their GP (doctor). NHS Direct says this is needed to provide safe treatment and care. As with all health records held in the NHS, these are confidential – they may be shared with other NHS professionals but only if this is needed because of the treatment involved, and only with your permission. Chapter 17 explains about getting access to any health records that the NHS holds about you (and explains what to do if you are acting on behalf of someone else).

Contacting NHS Direct can be helpful if you are uncertain what to do – for example, if you are not sure whether you should go to your GP or call an ambulance.

# NHS Direct Online

This is a website of information, as part of NHS Direct, available through a computer with Internet access. If you don't have such a computer, many public libraries provide computer terminals with Internet access. Some of these are available free; at others there may be a small charge to pay. There are also lots of local 'Internet cafés' around the country that you could use, although it is likely you will be asked to pay a fee (eg it might cost £5 for you to go on the Internet for 30 minutes).

Many local libraries, and some local Age Concerns, offer free training sessions on how to use the Internet. This usually involves your accessing (looking at) a website as part of the training. You might want to try looking at NHS Direct Online (see page 279) in your training session.

The website includes a health encyclopaedia that covers more than 400 topics, including different illnesses and conditions, tests, treatments (and a separate 'best treatments' section) and operations. NHS Direct Online also provides a database of hospitals and community health services, GPs, dentists, optometrists and pharmacies, and you can use it to find the details of your nearest service. It is also possible to complete and submit an online form setting out a particular query, if you cannot find the information you need on the website. This will be researched by a health-information professional and you should receive a response within five working days – but if you are feeling unwell and need immediate advice, contact the NHS Direct telephone service instead.

You will also find a link on NHS Direct's website to HealthSpace, an online service provided by the NHS for people aged 16 or over in England (www.healthspace.nhs.uk). If you want, you can use this secure website to keep a record of your own health details. There are plans to use the HealthSpace website as one of the ways to access Choose and Book, the new appointments booking system – see page 153. If you have a digital satellite television, you can use this to access NHS Direct with your TV remote control's 'Interactive' button. There are plans to make this NHS Digital Interactive package available through cable and Freeview TV services in late 2005.

## GP surgeries and out-of-hours services

Chapter 3 gives more details about seeing a GP, including registering with a particular surgery and out-of-hours services. Chapter 13 looks at your rights to NHS care if you are away from where you usually live (eg on holiday elsewhere in the UK). If you are not sure whether you should see a GP, you can ask NHS Direct for their advice, see a pharmacist, or attend a Walk-In Centre (see below). If any of these professionals feels it is necessary, they will advise you to go to a GP.

## NHS Walk-In Centres

NHS Walk-In Centres provide treatment for minor injuries and illnesses seven days a week. They are usually open from early in the morning until the evening. There is no need to make an appointment. An NHS nurse will see you. Walk-In centres can also provide details of out-of-hours GP and dental services, and details of other local health services, such as pharmacies. If your illness or injury is more serious, staff at the Centre will advise you what to do – they may even call an ambulance on your behalf if needed.

There are over 60 Walk-In Centres in England. You can find details of the one nearest to you by looking in your local telephone directory or by asking NHS Direct.

# Pharmacists

Pharmacists (or 'the chemist's') are experts on how medicines work. If you have any worries about the medicines you are taking, visit your nearest pharmacist, bringing the medicine bottle or packet with you so that he or she can see what you have been taking and when. Pharmacists can also advise on common illnesses such as coughs and colds, or on other health issues such as giving up smoking, and can also help you decide whether you need to see a doctor. You don't need to make an appointment to see a pharmacist, but you may need to wait a few minutes if they are busy with other customers (eg getting other people's prescriptions ready). As well as independent pharmacy (chemists) shops, found in most towns in the UK, major shops such as Boots The Chemist and Lloyds Chemists have pharmacy counters where you could also ask to speak to the pharmacist. Local newspapers often publish lists of the pharmacies offering out-of-hours services (usually on a rota basis: for example, one pharmacy offers this on a Tuesday night, another on a Wednesday and so on); or you can look in your local telephone book or contact NHS Direct for details.

See also Chapter 10.

# Hospital Accident & Emergency (A&E) units

A&E is one of the departments found in many (but not all) NHS hospitals. As their name suggests, they are intended for when emergency care is needed for serious injury or illness. The NHS regards an emergency as something that is a critical or life-threatening situation, such as:

- loss of consciousness;
- heavy blood loss;
- suspected broken bone(s);

- persistent chest pain for 15 minutes or more;
- difficulty breathing;
- overdose or poisoning.

If you are with someone who you think needs to go to A&E, you can either take them there yourself or you can call 999 for an emergency ambulance. If you are on your own, you may feel it is better to call for an ambulance than to try to get a lift from a friend or a taxi.

Calling for an ambulance won't necessarily mean that you are treated any more quickly when you arrive at A&E, however, as most departments assess you when you arrive and then treat the most urgent cases first. A&E departments have a team of doctors and nurses and, because they are generally part of a hospital, can admit you to other wards if needed.

The usual advice, if you are going to A&E, is not to eat, drink or smoke anything in case this delays any emergency treatment you need. A&E departments are open 24 hours a day, all year round. If you are not sure where your nearest A&E unit is, you can ask NHS Direct or look in the local telephone book.

## 999 calls and emergency services

Most people know that to obtain an ambulance you should telephone 999. This is a free call. The operator will ask you whether you require the police, fire brigade or ambulance, and will then connect you. You can also be connected if you ring NHS Direct and they think your situation requires an ambulance. The major work of the ambulance services is to get patients who have been seriously injured to hospital (usually A&E units) as quickly as possible because the treatment they need can only be provided there.

In the last few years, ambulance services have been finding it harder to meet their targets because of a huge rise in the numbers of hoax or unnecessary calls. Since October 2004, Ambulance Trusts do not have to respond to *all* calls. They will not have to respond to calls for people in non-urgent situations. For example, people who dial 999 and ask for an ambulance because they have a minor cut to their finger or earache, for example, will not automatically be sent an ambulance. Instead, Strategic Health Authorities and local Primary Care Trusts, together with the relevant Ambulance Trust, will have other options in place. This might involve local paramedics or an on-call doctor visiting and treating you at home, or (depending on why you have rung) it might be suggested you seek advice from NHS Direct or visit an NHS Walk-In Centre.

The ambulance service must respond to Category A or Category B emergency calls:

- **Category A** calls are for problems that are life-threatening, and the ambulance service aims to respond to them within eight minutes;
- **Category B** calls are where the problem is serious but not immediately life-threatening, and should be responded to within 14 minutes (in urban areas) or 19 minutes (in rural parts of the country).

Calls requesting the emergency services are often recorded.

Ambulance services also provide transport for complicated hospital admissions, discharges and transfers. This type of non-emergency work is carried out by the Patient Transport Service (PTS) – see Chapter 12. It also provides transport for hospital day care for older people, along with other people who need to attend a hospital for out-patient appointments or treatment and whose illness or disability means other forms of transport are not an option. Patient Transport Service arrangements usually need to be booked in advance. They are not available through the 999 telephone number. If your admission to or discharge from hospital is more routine, you will probably be expected to make your own arrangements – perhaps getting a lift from a friend or neighbour, or using a taxi. Voluntary organisations such as the British Red Cross can sometimes help people who cannot use or do not have access to public or private transport and need to get to a health appointment or return home from hospital.

## Minor Injuries Units

An appropriate alternative to A&E for some people is a Minor Injuries Unit, where treatment is led by nurses. These units are for patients with injuries such as:

- sprains, cuts and grazes;
- infected wounds;
- bites and stings;
- broken bones;
- minor head injuries.

You do not need an appointment to visit a Minor Injuries Unit but, if you are not sure whether A&E or some other route would be more appropriate, you can telephone NHS Direct and ask for their advice. These units tend to be part of a hospital – including hospitals with A&E departments. Unlike A&E departments, they are not all open all the time – for example, they may be open between 8am and 10pm.

## Keeping healthy

Although we all need some health services from time to time – even if this is only for flu vaccinations or check-ups with the dentist – most people would like to stay as healthy as they can for as long as they can. There is lots of information and advice available for anyone who wants to try to improve or maintain their health.

Age Concern Factsheet 45 *Staying healthy in later life* will help to point you in the right direction.

# Chapter 3

# GPs and primary care services

Most NHS services are divided into two types – primary care and secondary care. *Primary care* is the term used to describe treatment and care from general practitioners (GPs) and other community-based professionals such as dentists, district nurses, chiropodists and occupational therapists. *Secondary care* describes the more specialist care that you would expect to find in hospital – there is more about this in Chapters 11 and 12. This chapter concentrates on some aspects of primary care. There is more about occupational therapy in Chapter 7, and more about chiropody in Chapter 9.

## GP services

Since 1 April 2004, the vast majority of GPs have been working to a changed national NHS contract. This is the contract that GPs agree to sign with their local Primary Care Trust (PCT). It sets out the services they will provide to NHS patients from their premises (the surgery, health centre or clinic) and at the patient's home where necessary.

Some GP surgeries are run by only one doctor – these are known as solo or single-handed practices. This type of arrangement has become less common in recent years, as it is felt that doctors (and patients) benefit from working with other colleagues rather than on their own; it can be popular with those patients who prefer to have only one doctor involved in their care, although there will always be times when another doctor has to be seen because the solo GP is away or not on call.

Most practices are formal partnerships (as might exist in other businesses) owned by two or more individual GPs.

A few GPs are employed direct by the Primary Care Trust – they are sometimes called salaried doctors. Some GPs who are partners in their practice may also employ a doctor to work for them.

There are also GP services available through what is called the Personal Medical Service (PMS). This arrangement, which began in 1998, is another way of providing NHS general practice.

Everyone who lives in the UK is entitled to register with an NHS GP practice. This right is based on whether you are living permanently in the UK, not what nationality you are or where your passport was issued. This includes people living in care homes (see Chapter 13).

Some people who are UK citizens no longer live in the UK but have decided to live abroad – perhaps in Spain or France. They have different rights, discussed in Chapter 13.

## Registering with a practice

Under the previous arrangements, before April 2004 you registered with a particular GP at the surgery where he or she worked – and joined that GP's list of patients. If one GP's 'list' was full, you might be asked to register with a different GP at the same practice. When you rang for an appointment, you might well have been asked who your GP was, so an appointment could be made for you to see that person.

The arrangements since April 2004 are slightly different. Instead of registering with one particular GP, you are now registered with the practice. This means it is the practice that holds the list of patients, rather than the individual GPs who work there. If you register as a new patient, you should be asked if you want to say which GP would be your 'preferred' doctor (you can also name a preferred practitioner who is not a doctor but works as part of the practice team, such as a specialist nurse). Your choice should be recorded in writing, and as far as possible you should be able to see that person when you make an appointment. But it doesn't give you a right to insist on seeing that doctor or nurse every time. If they are away, for example, or cannot fit you in when you are free, you will be offered an appointment with another doctor or nurse at the practice as appropriate.

If you are having problems finding a surgery to register with, get in touch with your local Primary Care Trust. It is responsible for making sure you are registered. You can find it in your telephone book or by contacting NHS Direct (page 279).

## Appointments

Since the end of 2004, everyone has the right to expect to be able to see a GP within two working days, or another primary care professional (such as the practice nurse) within one working day of requesting an appointment.

You may find that your appointment with the GP will be expected to be concluded within 5–10 minutes. Some people take with them a list of questions or concerns they want to raise with the GP about their health, to make sure they remember everything they want to say. You may also find it helpful to write down what the GP has told you as soon as you can. It is very easy to get some details wrong when remembering what was said. If later on you can't remember an important point, you can always ring the surgery, explain you have forgotten and ask to speak to the doctor you saw if they are available when you ring. You can then ask the GP to tell you again what was discussed.

If you are taken ill when you are visiting somewhere else in the UK and need to see a GP, you can go to any NHS surgery and ask to be registered as a temporary patient. You 'count' as a temporary resident in the new area if you have been there for more than 24 hours but less than three months. In a medical emergency you can also ask a GP to provide treatment without needing to register. If you are taken ill away from home and don't know where the GP practices are and cannot find a local telephone book, ring NHS Direct to find out.

## Changing practices

You can ask to change practices – in fact, you don't need to ask at the current practice. If you want to go to a different practice, ask the new surgery if they will take you on as a patient. If they agree, they will contact your last GP to ask for your notes to be transferred over. You don't have to let your previous GP know but it would be polite to do so.

Many people change practices because they move to a different area. Some people might decide to change practices because they are unhappy with some aspect of the surgery's care. It's always worth telling the practice manager, or a GP or nurse at the surgery, why you are unhappy. They may be able to resolve this with you. They should also tell you about the complaints system they must offer (see Chapter 16).

## Being removed from a practice's list

Occasionally, a patient is asked to leave the practice. This might happen if a patient has been violent or abusive towards a member of staff or to other patients in the waiting area. If this cannot be sorted out, as a last resort the patient may be asked to find another practice. If this affects you, contact the local Primary Care Trust as well as the Patient Advice and Liaison Service (PALS). The Primary Care Trust must provide general practice services for you; the Patient Advice and Liaison Service may be able to suggest ways you could receive this other than going to a particular surgery. Or it may be that alternative arrangements are offered together with some support or treatment to help with aggressive behaviour.

Although your GP is not obliged to tell you why you are being asked to leave the practice, many do so as this information can be helpful. But you cannot be asked to leave because of your age or because your health needs are high. If you thought this had happened, you would have grounds for a complaint – see Chapter 16.

## The practice team

All surgeries offer the same sort of basic primary care medicine. This includes:

- diagnoses;
- prescribing medicine;
- health checks;
- referring you to other NHS services (such as to hospital);
- providing inoculations (eg flu vaccinations).

Different surgeries may offer other services as well, such as:

- minor surgery (such as removing a wart);
- cervical cancer screening.

Many practices also employ a nurse who carries out some screening and treatment services. In a few cases, he or she may also visit you at home, if you need regular monitoring or nursing help. It is more likely, though, that the GP will arrange for the local NHS community nursing service to get involved.

The surgery should have a leaflet that tells you what services are offered, and gives the surgery's opening hours, contact details, and what to do if you are taken ill when the surgery is closed (see page 44).

A few GP practices have arranged with their local social services departments to have a social worker available at the surgery. The social worker is employed by social services but runs specific sessions at the surgery or clinic, or has appointments available for you to see him or her there. If your GP thinks this would help you – perhaps because you need advice about care services or help with completing a welfare benefit application – they will suggest you arrange to see the social worker. The idea behind having a social worker at the surgery is that this makes it easier for patients who might otherwise have to make a separate trip to social services' offices. Even if your surgery doesn't have a social worker based there, your GP might still suggest that you talk to someone from social services, if this is appropriate for you.

You may find other staff available to help as needed at the practice, such as nurse practitioners and specialist nurses to support patients with specific conditions such as diabetes or asthma.

*If you are registered with a practice, you are entitled to receive any of the services it provides for its NHS patients. This applies regardless of whether you are living in your own home, in a sheltered flat, with relatives in their home, or in a care home or in a care home offering nursing care (see Chapter 13).*

## Referrals

Your GP may prescribe medicine for you, or give you advice and information to help you deal with a particular health problem. Or he or she may want to refer you to a more specialised doctor. This will either be a consultant, often based at a hospital, or it might be a GP with Special Interests (GPwSI). A GPwSI may work at the same surgery or be based at another clinic or health centre. They have chosen to specialise in care for a particular health area, such as dermatology (skin conditions – eg eczema), or ear, nose and throat conditions, with the aim of making it easier for patients to receive appropriate treatment more quickly.

---

### Box 7. Second opinions

You have the right to *ask* for a second opinion – but you can't *insist* that one be provided. It is up to the doctor you ask (usually either a GP or a hospital consultant) to arrange this. Generally, most doctors will arrange for a second opinion for you. Indeed, your GP or consultant may decide they would like a second opinion if they are not sure what the problem might be, or are unclear why a treatment isn't working as well as it should. Asking for another professional's view should help. You can also ask for a second opinion on behalf of someone else, but you must have his or her permission to do so.

Because there's no automatic right to a second opinion, there are no time limits within which one must be provided. If a second opinion is needed because of a medical priority, an appointment with another consultant or GP will be made as soon as possible.

---

Your GP may also refer you to the local NHS community health services. In some areas, you can also contact the community health services yourself without involving your GP. The sorts of services they may provide include a:

■ chiropodist (see Chapter 9);

- physiotherapist (see Chapter 7);
- community psychiatric nurse (see Chapter 8);
- hospice at home or Macmillan nurse (see Chapter 15).

Or your GP may refer you to the local intermediate care service (see Chapter 7) or to the district nursing or health visitor services (see page 44).

The GP may also refer you to the local continence service (Box 8) – or, in some areas, you may approach the service direct. There are two types of incontinence, urine (or bladder) and faecal (or bowel). Typical problems with urine incontinence include 'leaking', or not emptying your bladder fully each time, or needing to go to the toilet very frequently. Problems with bowel incontinence include being constipated or having diarrhoea.

---

**Box 8. Continence services**

Your local Primary Care Trust (PCT) must run an integrated continence service. It must set criteria to decide who can receive what type of continence supplies or aids, or advice from a continence adviser. The criteria must be available to the public. They apply whether you live in your own home, in a sheltered flat, or in a care home (including those offering nursing care). There is more about NHS services for care home residents in Chapter 13.

The type of continence help the NHS can give includes:

- A diagnosis, so you know what is causing the problem.
- Advice about what to eat and drink, to help your bladder and bowels perform more effectively.

---

- Clothing that you can remove quickly and easily to aid your using the toilet.
- Reviewing your current medication to see if this is causing the problem or making it worse.
- Pelvic floor exercises to help your internal muscles and keep better control.
- Providing continence pads, aids and other supplies.

The advice and supplies are free from the NHS. Commodes are usually available from the Joint Equipment Stores (see page 99, sometimes also called the Community Equipment Store). The NHS or social services may offer a laundry service. The continence service will be able to tell you about this.

Age Concern Factsheet 23 *Help with continence* has further details.

Since April 2005 GP practices have been able to commission some services for you direct, but it is up to each practice whether to do this. It means that the practice where you are registered as a patient can choose either to buy the NHS care you need or to refer you to the services commissioned (arranged) by your Primary Care Trust. Whichever arrangement is used should make no difference to the quality and speed of NHS treatment you receive.

## Home visits

Your GP should visit you at home (including the care home where you live) if you are too ill to get to the surgery. Your GP should also visit you at home if you cannot leave the person you provide care for in order to get to the surgery, because they are too ill to be left alone. When you ring the surgery, explain in as much detail as you can why you cannot get to the surgery so that staff can decide whether or not to visit you at home.

## NHS services you can be charged for

Many primary care services are provided free of charge through the NHS. These include visits to the doctor or nurse, and any advice or treatment they provide. But you may have to pay for some services. These include several services you might ask your GP to carry out. They include some (but not all) travel or holiday vaccinations. They can also include medical reports for insurance and driving purposes. Ask your GP how much the charge will be beforehand.

There are some services you might have to pay for because they are not always available from the NHS; for example, complementary therapies such as acupuncture, osteopathy, reflexology or homoeopathy. Even if your GP thinks that one of these may help you, there is not much of this type of support available on the NHS. There may be some exceptions for people who are terminally ill or have severe, long-term conditions. Although there are no guarantees that the NHS will provide these therapies for you, you can always ask.

If a service is not available to you on the NHS, your GP may suggest alternatives or even tell you if he or she knows of a local practitioner. Note that if you are an NHS patient your GP should not put pressure on you to accept private treatment; they cannot recommend private practitioners. If you decide to find a local practitioner privately, you would need to contact that person and arrange to see them in their private clinic, and pay whatever they charge. Make sure you know what this might cost before agreeing to a session. Many complementary therapists charge a larger sum for the first visit, as this tends to take longer than subsequent visits because they use it to find out the detail of what has been happening for you.

Thirteen types of professional therapist are registered by the Health Professions Council (see page 274). These include physiotherapists and chiropodists. There are plans for acupuncturists also to be registered. In each case this requires an Act of Parliament to be passed, since to make it illegal to practise without registration there must first be a law requiring this.

# Out-of-hours services

Since December 2004, Primary Care Trusts have been responsible for 'out-of-hours' primary care. Part of the contract that GPs have now to provide NHS services allows them to decide not to provide out-of-hours services. Instead, between the hours of 6.30pm and 8am Monday to Friday, and at weekends and Bank holidays, other arrangements may be in place. What is available varies from place to place, and may still involve GPs who have decided that they would like to provide an out-of-hours service.

There are out-of-hours services in all parts of the country, and your practice must be able to tell you what this is (perhaps in a leaflet, or a poster at the surgery). You may find little difference between these new arrangements and what used to happen before December 2004. This is because in many parts of the country under the old arrangements you would not in any case have seen your own GP out-of-hours.

# Community nursing services

Primary Care Trusts provide the community nursing services in each area. They employ a range of district nurses to carry this out and, in some cases, also employ specialist health visitors (often called Health Visitors for the Elderly or for Older People. Most other health visitors work with babies and young children).

District nurses provide nursing care to people who live in their own home, in sheltered housing or in care homes (Chapter 13 has more about this). There is no minimum amount of nursing that you might receive at home – it all depends on your need for care and the priorities of your Primary Care Trust. District nurses can help with things such as:

- care of pressure sores (including taking steps to prevent them from happening);
- artificial feeding tubes;
- blood pressure and other monitoring.

They may become more involved in your care during periods of severe illness, or if someone is coming to the end of their life (see also Chapter 15). District nursing services from the NHS are free.

In recent years, the type of support that a district nurse might provide through the NHS has changed. Some care is now carried out, free, by health care assistants under the supervision of the district nurse. But some care provision has gradually moved over to social services departments. This often includes bathing services – where someone helps you take a bath because you cannot do this alone. However, if you feel that the NHS should be providing, free of charge, the type of support you are being asked to pay towards, you may want to contact Age Concern (see page 264) to make sure that what has been arranged is correct and to how to challenge this local policy.

Where social services departments arrange a service such as help to bathe, you may be asked to pay. Each department sets the amount it charges, but there are some rules about this.

---

Age Concern Factsheet 46 *Paying for care and support at home* explains what these charges are.

---

Sometimes people decide to pay privately for a nurse at home. It is up to you whether you want to do this, and it is up the nurse or the agency (if they work for an agency) how much this will cost. Agencies that provide nurses or care workers who carry out personal tasks must be registered under the Care Standards Act 2000. But, unlike private health clinics and hospitals, these agencies are registered with the Commission for Social Care Inspection (CSCI; see page 269 for contact details).

The agency should provide you with written details about its services, and you should agree a contract with it. Details of local private agencies can be found in your local telephone directory. Or you can contact the United Kingdom Home Care Association (UKHCA; address on page 283), whose member organisations provide care at home. UKHCA also has a leaflet, *Choosing care in your home*, which you may find helpful.

In January 2005 the Government announced plans to create a new NHS professional: the community matron. Community matrons will work with people who have long-term conditions, such as diabetes, asthma and arthritis, providing one-to-one support. The plan is for there to be 3,000 community matrons by March 2007. They will form part of the National Service Framework for Long-Term Conditions, expected to be published in 2005 (see page 16).

# Private doctors

Some primary care doctors have their own, private, practices. In this case, you register with them as a private patient. This means you have to pay each time you see them, and you may also have to pay for any medicines they prescribe for you. It is up to doctors who practise privately whether to offer a repeat prescription service (see also Chapter 10).

How much you are charged is up to the doctor, as for any private business. Make sure you know how much the visits and other treatment and items cost before agreeing to them. If you have private health care insurance, ask your insurer whether the cost of private primary health care is included.

# Chapter 4

# Dentistry

This chapter explains your right to an NHS dentist (and how to find one and stay on their list); emergency NHS dental care; and your entitlement to different types of dental care, such as check-ups, crowns and dentures. It also covers paying for NHS dental care, the role of other dental personnel and dentistry services provided in NHS hospitals. How to complain about dental services, dentists and dental staff is explained in Chapter 16.

It also briefly covers private dentistry in terms of cost and payments, standards and cosmetic treatment. You may also want to read Age Concern Factsheet 5 *Dental care and older people*.

## Finding and keeping an NHS dentist

In some parts of the country, finding an NHS dentist has become more and more difficult. Some people have found that their dentist, whom they might have visited for many years, has decided not to offer treatment under the NHS any more but will accept them as private patients instead.

Most dentists run their own businesses, so it is up to each dentist whether or not to offer treatments under the NHS. Dentists who offer NHS treatment do so under a contract with an NHS body. In the past, this has been the local Health Authority or, more recently, the Strategic

Health Authority. There are proposals for dentists to have contracts with their local Primary Care Trust (PCT) to provide NHS dental care from October 2005. Under this arrangement, the Primary Care Trust would pay the dentists for the NHS treatment they provided.

Most NHS patients pay something towards the cost of their treatment – these amounts are set by government and are explained on page 57.

A small number of dentists are 'salaried'. This means they are full-time NHS employees. They often work for the local Community Dental Service, explained on page 52. Salaried dentists are not allowed to offer private treatments to their NHS patients.

There are several ways you can find an NHS dentist. The first is to contact NHS Direct (see page 279). NHS Direct will be able to tell you about dental practices in your area that are taking on new NHS patients.

One of the difficulties people often face is that the nearest available NHS dentist is some miles from where they live. Although you have a right to be registered with an NHS dentist, there is nothing that says you must be found one where you live. This means that, if the only practice taking on NHS patients near you is in the next town, you may have to register there. Nevertheless, you can raise with the local Patient Advice and Liaison Service (PALS) any concerns you have about the lack of NHS dentists nearer to where you live. Each Primary Care Trust has a Patient Advice and Liaison Service you can contact (see page 227 for more details).

If you need a dentist to visit you at home, perhaps because you have a disability or have other health problems, make sure you tell NHS Direct this when asking for an NHS dentist. It will be able to tell you which dentists offer home visits.

You can also search NHS Direct's website for details of NHS dentists, under 'local services database'. If you select 'dental practices' and enter your postcode, this will give you a list of local practices, including those that were registering new NHS patients when last contacted by NHS Direct. Or you can contact your local Primary Care Trust, and ask them for help in finding a dentist willing to take on NHS patients.

Some dentists advertise themselves as taking on new NHS patients. These ads might be in local telephone directories (under 'Dental services') or in local newspapers.

Neighbours and friends in your area might be able to recommend the dentist with whom they are registered as NHS patients. You could then contact that dental surgery and ask if they are taking on new NHS patients. Some dental surgeries offer to put you on a waiting list. This is nothing to do with waiting times set by government for treatment. Rather, it is something that individual dentists have decided to do: they will have only a certain number of NHS patients 'on their books' at any one time – but they will put your details on a waiting list, so that when a 'vacancy' arises (as when someone moves away, for example), you can be accepted in their place.

Some people can inadvertently lose their status as an NHS patient. This is because, when a dentist accepts you as an NHS patient, he or she does so for a period of about 15 months. If you see your dentist within the 15 months, your registration as an NHS patient continues. As a registered patient, your dentist gives you what is called 'continuing care' (this is not the same as continuing health care, described in Chapter 13; it just means that the dentist carries on providing care to you as needed while you are registered at his or her surgery). If you do not see your dentist again within this period, you may lose your registration with that practice. This means the dentist can decide to remove you from his or her list. If you have not attended your dentist for regular NHS dental care within the past 15 months, you should contact the practice to make sure you are still on its register of NHS patients.

In October 2004 the National Institute for Health and Clinical Excellence (NICE) issued new guidance about how frequently you should see your dentist for an NHS check-up. For example, some people who have very good oral health (teeth, gums and mouth) may not need to go for a routine check-up as often as every six months – see page 55. Because this change had not begun at the time of writing, it is not yet clear whether it might affect the 15 months 'rule', explained above.

# Emergency NHS dental care

If you are registered with a dental practice as an NHS patient, that surgery should give you details of its emergency treatment arrangements. If you can, try to contact your dentist during usual surgery hours, as treatment will be easier if surgery staff are available. The surgery's answerphone, which will be switched on when the surgery is closed, should also give details of what to do if you need emergency dental care.

Dentists must make what are called 'reasonable arrangements' to ensure that their registered patients receive emergency care and treatment as soon as possible. This will either be from them or from another dentist. 'Reasonable arrangements' include that the treatment is within 24 hours of the original request.

If you are not registered with a dentist for NHS treatment, you can contact a surgery near to you and ask if they would be willing to treat you as an emergency NHS patient. They can refuse, however, so you may find it simpler to contact NHS Direct, which will be able to tell you about local emergency arrangements. These might include an NHS Dental Access Centre (which exist in some parts of England) or a rota of local dentists.

Emergencies can arise for a range of reasons. They could include raging toothache, a filling that has fallen out, a damaged crown or more serious issues. Injuries or accidents to the face may require emergency dental surgery in hospital. If you are at all unsure what to do, or how serious your particular emergency might be, contact NHS Direct for advice.

Some emergencies arise during usual surgery hours. But some may arise at night or at weekends – what are often called 'out of hours'. From October 2005, Primary Care Trusts are responsible for arranging out-of-hours services. It is up to each local one to establish what this means in practice in your area. Some Primary Care Trusts may arrange for this service to be carried out by local dentists, by the Community Dental Service, or through another arrangement. But there *must* be an out-of-hours NHS dental service in your area; NHS Direct will be able to tell you whom to contact.

Emergencies for private patients are explained later, under 'Private dentistry'. Even if you usually receive private dental care, however, you can still ask for emergency NHS treatment.

## Home visits for NHS patients

Arrangements for people who cannot get to a dentist because of poor health or disability vary from one part of the country to another. If you are unable to visit the surgery where you are registered as an NHS patient because of health problems, your dentist must visit you at home and not charge you extra for doing so, provided you live within five miles of the surgery. Local Community Dental Services may also provide NHS treatment for people in their own homes or those living in sheltered housing or care homes. (Care homes may have their own arrangements; ask the care home manager about this. See also Chapter 13.) In rural areas there may be mobile dental services. NHS Direct will have the details of these local arrangements.

Anyone who receives NHS treatment at home will still have to pay the same charges that would have applied if they had visited the surgery (see page 57).

## NHS dental treatments

As with any treatment, precisely what you need in the way of dental care will depend on the state of your teeth, gums and mouth. Dentists who undertake NHS treatment must offer you all the necessary treatment that is available under the NHS to make and keep your mouth healthy (your 'oral health'). It should also be 'within the competence of the dentist providing it' – a dentist should only offer you treatments that he or she is capable of providing.

There are, however, some treatments that are not available on the NHS. These include cosmetic treatments such as teeth whitening or tooth-coloured crowns on back teeth. If you want these treatments, you will probably have to pay privately for this (see later, under 'Private dentistry').

If you are a new NHS patient, your dentist will carry out an examination, inspecting your mouth, teeth and gums, and possibly will decide to take some x-rays or impressions of your teeth. The information gained will be used to draw up a treatment plan for you (Box 9). Many dentists offering NHS treatment also offer private dental care. If you wanted something that was not available on the NHS, and the dentist was willing to undertake this treatment, your treatment plan should set out what this private work entails and how much it might cost as well as any details of NHS treatments. Note that it is not possible to have both NHS and private treatment on the same tooth during the same course of treatment.

---

**Box 9. Dental treatment plans**

The treatment plan is free and you should be given a copy. Treatment plans should be provided to registered NHS patients:

■ when you are first accepted by a dentist for treatment;
■ when both NHS and private treatments will be provided in the same course of treatment;
■ when treatments such as dentures, crowns or bridges are being provided;
■ whenever you ask for one.

---

Your treatment plan will set out how many visits you might need to make in order to complete that course of treatment. For example, if you needed several fillings or crowns on both sides of your mouth, the dentist might advise that these be carried out over two or three separate occasions if doing them in one visit would mean having to keep your mouth open for uncomfortably long periods of time. On the other hand, your course of treatment might simply involve a check-up and a 'scale and polish' (a particular way of cleaning teeth). Once the course of treatment is completed, the dentist will advise you when you should come for your next check-up.

For many years, the standard advice has been to go to your dentist for a check-up every six months. More recently, some dental experts have questioned whether everyone always needs to go that regularly.

People whose oral health (of their teeth, gums and mouth) is very good might need to go only once a year – or even once every two years. In October 2004 the National Institute for Health and Clinical Excellence issued advice about how often NHS patients should have a routine check-up. NICE has now said that this should vary according to what each patient needs. For everyone aged 18 or over the minimum time between routine checks should be three months and the maximum time two years. The basic rule of thumb is that the better your oral health the longer the time between routine check-ups. NICE has asked that local health communities review their existing practice and work out how quickly this change to routine check-ups can be put into place. But, regardless of this advice or what your dentist suggests to you, if something begins to worry you about your teeth or gums, make an appointment straight away – don't delay until the next check-up visit is due.

## Oral health

Although most of us think of going to the dentist in terms of our teeth, dentists are expert in the health of our whole mouth (oral health). They often detect early signs of oral cancer, for example, or other serious health problems. Even if our teeth appear to be fine, following the advice of your dentist should help you maintain and improve your overall oral health. A dentist can also refer you to more specialised NHS services if needed – for example, to see an NHS consultant at an ear, nose and throat (ENT) hospital department.

## Dental professionals

Dentists usually employ dental nurses and assistants to help them with their work. Dental nurses may make up the formula used in fillings, for example, and assist in a variety of other ways.

The General Dental Council (GDC) keeps up-to-date registers of dentists, dental hygienists and dental therapists who are qualified to practise dentistry in the UK. These are called The Dentists Register and The Rolls of Dental Auxiliaries. It is illegal to practise dentistry without being registered with the General Dental Council – except for doctors who are registered with the General Medical Council and are working in non-NHS dentistry.

# Paying for NHS dental care

For many years (almost since the beginning of the NHS), the NHS has been asking patients to contribute towards the cost of the care they receive individually. These are standard amounts that all patients pay for NHS dental care – except for some people, who may pay less (or nothing at all) because they have a low income. The NHS Low Income Scheme applies to all adults – not just older people – and is explained on pages 96–98.

There are some NHS dental treatments for which no one pays:

- repairs to dentures;
- the stopping of bleeding;
- re-cementing a bridge;
- calling out a dentist to a surgery in an emergency, or for a home visit if needed (note that it is the 'call-out' that is free – not the treatment provided when the dentist sees you).

Dentists do not usually charge for adjustments to NHS treatments if these are needed within a short time of the original treatment. Examples include a tooth still being uncomfortable a few days after a filling or dentures needing adjusting in the first few weeks after they have been fitted. However, if dentures become loose a few months after being fitted and need to be readjusted because of natural changes to the gums, this can count as a new course of treatment. If so, there will be further charges to pay – ask your dentist about this when your dentures are first being fitted.

## How much does NHS dentistry cost?

The costs of NHS dental treatments, like other NHS charges, are set by the government of the day. This means they are the same no matter where in England you live. The total amount you pay will depend on:

■ The actual treatment you receive.
■ Whether you are eligible for any help with these costs (as set out on page 93).

The government also sets a maximum amount you will be asked to pay for any single course of treatment. In England from 1 May 2004, no one has been asked to pay more than £378 for a single course of NHS dental care.

Examples of the charges you have to pay for individual treatments are, at 1 May 2004:

■ Basic check-up (sometimes called an examination)    £5.64
■ Extensive clinical examination    £8.44
■ Simple scale and polish of your teeth    £8.88
■ two small x-rays and one small filling, *from*    £9.88
■ one precious-metal crown, *from*    £89.24
■ an upper or lower metal denture, *from*    £107.76
■ full set of plastic dentures, *from*    £122.32

Your dentist collects the amount that you pay for your NHS dental care. New charges may apply from later in 2005. To find out if the amounts have changed and, if so, what they are, you can ask your dental surgery or contact Age Concern.

# Private dentistry

As mentioned above, there is no state help towards the costs of private dentistry. This makes it very important that you know how much you might have to pay for any dental care you receive privately before you agree to starting the treatment.

Everyone is entitled to receive NHS dental care; but some people have decided – either as a positive choice or because they have not felt able to accept the NHS service offered to them – to become private patients. Many dentists offering NHS treatments also offer private care – this can become confusing, so be clear about whether you are registered as a private patient or an NHS patient, and whether the treatment you are agreeing to will be provided through the NHS or privately.

Remember that not all dental treatments are available on the NHS. You may be registered as an NHS patient but decide to have some extra, private, care from the same dentist. Bear in mind that the NHS does not allow both NHS and private treatment to be carried out on the same tooth during the same course of treatment. If that happened, you would have to pay for all the treatment on that tooth as a private patient.

If you are registered as an NHS patient and you decide to go ahead with a mix of private and NHS treatment during the same course of dental care, your dentist will need you to sign to agree to this.

Unlike the charges for NHS dentistry set out above, it is up to each dentist how much they charge for private treatment. The amount you will be asked to pay may vary from one dentist to another. These costs are likely to be more than the NHS would charge. Do make sure you are certain how much you will be asked to pay before agreeing to go ahead.

Sometimes it may be difficult for a dentist to give you an exact cost –
some procedures may be easier than expected, or the dentist may
discover unknown problems once they start the treatment. But you
could ask the dentist for the 'worst case' and 'best case' scenarios –
in other words, ask what the highest cost would be as well as the
lowest cost. This will give you as good an idea as possible of how
much you might have to pay.

There are some health insurance companies that offer dental
insurance plans to cover at least some of the costs of private dental
treatment. Some dentists will take on patients who are members of
particular schemes – your dentist will be able to tell you about this.

## Dentistry in hospital

The vast majority of people receive primary dental care – that is, they
see their dentist in his or her local surgery or practice. Some NHS
dentistry is, however, provided in hospital. This can include:

- removal of some wisdom teeth;
- work to teeth and gums following facial injury, or for a disability
  that affects the jaw;
- any dental treatment that requires a general anaesthetic.

Your dentist or your GP can refer you to NHS hospital dental services
if he or she thinks this is necessary. There is no charge for NHS
hospital services, including dentistry.

## Anaesthetics

There are lots of different ways that dentists can make treatments
pain-free. They might use creams or injections to numb the area, for
example. Or a general anaesthetic might be used to sedate you
during treatment, particularly if you are having a lot of treatment in
one go (such as having lots of teeth extracted during one session).

Dentists also use a technique called conscious sedation. This means that you are given drugs that stop you feeling pain but you are able to understand what is happening and respond to questions that the dentist asks. Private dental clinics that provide general anaesthesia are regulated under the Care Standards Act 2000. This means they are registered and inspected by the Healthcare Commission (which also inspects such services from the NHS).

## Public health

Primary Care Trusts are responsible for dental public health. This means they have a duty to assess the overall picture of dental health in each area and to commission services to meet this need. There might be particular problems locally – for example, very poor dental health among some schoolchildren, or particular groups of older people, or homeless people. Examples of the services a Primary Care Trust might commission include health-promotion schemes reminding people to have their teeth checked, or explaining what 'good oral health' looks like, or trying to improve people's access to NHS dental services. Or they may look at schemes to fluoridate local water supplies. You can ask your Primary Care Trust what steps it is taking with regard to dental public health in your area.

# Chapter 5

# Eye services

This chapter explores eyesight, including free eye tests and getting and paying for equipment such as contact lenses, contact lens solution and spectacles. It looks at referrals to eye specialists; your rights if you have or your family has a history of glaucoma or diabetes; and referrals for surgery.

It also considers paying privately for treatments such as laser treatment to correct short sight, paying privately for glasses and contact lenses, and getting a guide dog and other support.

## Sight problems

There are a number of different sight problems. Some affect both children and adults, others are more likely to happen as we grow older. Common problems include (in alphabetical order):

- **Astigmatism** Both distance and near vision are affected. People with this may have headaches or be very sensitive to light.
- **Cataracts** More than half of people aged over 65 are likely to have some cataract development at some stage. Cataracts occur when part of the eye – the lens – becomes cloudy. This cloudiness stops light passing through the lens to the back of the eye, and vision becomes dim or blurred. Over time, vision may

change colour (becoming more yellow), or you may see double images, or have particularly poor vision in bright light.

- **Diabetic retinopathy** Diabetes can affect the blood vessels in the retina, as well as affecting sight in other ways (it is one cause of cataracts).

- **Glaucoma** When pressure inside the eye becomes raised, the optic nerve can become damaged. This reduces the field of vision (how widely we can see) and the ability to see clearly.

- **Long sightedness (hypermetropia)** With long sight, light is focused beyond the retina and the eye has to compensate to re-focus. This makes it difficult to see things close up. Reading may become very difficult and, for older people, there can also be blurred distance vision.

- **Macular degeneration** The macula, which is at the centre of the retina, can become damaged and stop working. Because this often happens in later life, it is also called age-related macular degeneration.

- **Presbyopia (ageing eye)** As we get older, the lens of the eye thickens and begins to lose flexibility. As a result, we lose the ability to focus on objects that are close up.

- **Short sightedness (myopia)** This happens when light is focused in front of the retina and causes anything some distance away (eg a cinema screen) to look blurred. Near vision, however, is usually clear – for example, there are usually no problems in reading a book.

There are many treatments and solutions for problems such as those listed above. They range from glasses (spectacles) or contact lenses that correct your vision, to surgery to remove cataracts (commonly carried out as day surgery, where there is no need for an overnight stay).

Eyesight can change quickly or slowly. Sometimes we are not aware straight away that damage is happening to the eye. So it is important to get your sight checked regularly, and to see an eye care professional as soon as anything about your eyesight begins to change.

## Sight tests

Everyone aged 60 or over is entitled to a free sight test on the NHS. Tests are carried out by local optometrists. Even though we still call them 'the optician's', if you go to a high street practice, you will have your eyes examined either by an optometrist or an ophthalmic medical practitioner (OMP) – see Box 10.

---

**Box 10. Different terms for 'sight professionals'**

There are a number of terms used to describe different professionals specialising in sight. 'Optician' is a term we are all familiar with, but in fact it describes:

- **Ophthalmic opticians** (also called optometrists), who are qualified to examine eyes, recognise disease, and prescribe and fit spectacles (glasses) and contact lenses.
- **Dispensing opticians** are qualified to fit spectacles, and may have additional qualifications to enable them to fit contact lenses too (in which case they may call themselves 'Contact lens opticians').
- **Manufacturing opticians**, who make spectacles.

Everyone who examines eyes or fits and dispenses (gives out) spectacles and contact lenses has to be registered to do this by the General Optical Council. This registration means that these professionals have adequate training, qualifications

---

and practical experience. It is an offence to practise as a dispensing optician without being registered. If someone is found guilty and convicted, they can be fined up to £2,500.

There are also other terms you may come across:

- **Ophthalmologists** specialise in the treatment of eye diseases. They are medically qualified and work mostly in eye hospitals and hospital eye departments.
- **Orthoptists** work with ophthalmologists to assess squints and double vision, for example, before treatment. They are then involved in monitoring the treatment.

Ophthalmic medical practitioners often work in practices called 'Medical Eye Centres'. They are doctors who have chosen to specialise in examining eyes. Many optometrists run their own, private, businesses. Some work for larger chains such as SpecSaver, or run the optical services in larger chemists' stores, such as Boots The Chemist.

When you make an appointment, make sure the optometrist knows this is for an NHS sight test. The test may include checking the pressure in your eyes, as well as your ability to read letters at long and short distances. Tests for older people may also include conditions such as glaucoma and cataract.

If you are the parent, brother, sister, son or daughter of someone with glaucoma, and you are aged 40 or over, you are entitled to a free NHS eye test. If you are under the age of 60, and have been either diagnosed as having glaucoma or told by an ophthalmologist that you are at risk of glaucoma, you are also entitled to a free NHS sight test. Leaflet HC11 *Help with health costs*, which can be obtained from the post office or the optometrist or the Department of Health (see page 270), explains who else is eligible for free NHS tests. This includes people under the age of 60 with diabetes.

When you go for your sight test, tell the optometrist if you are entitled to a free NHS test. If you are claiming because you are aged 60 or over, you may need to take with you an official document that proves your age. Examples of such proof include your birth certificate, passport, a travel concession card (eg your train or bus pass), or your NHS medical card (this is the card given to you when you first need to register with a GP as a patient).

In recent years, the Government has been trying to reduce the numbers of people falsely claiming free NHS tests. This is why people are now asked for proof. If you make a claim but are in fact not eligible for a free sight test, you could end up being fined up to £100 as well as having to pay the original fee for the eyesight test. In some cases you could even face prosecution, under the Health Act 1999.

Although most people have their sight test carried out at the optometrist's premises, he or she could visit you where you live. They can (but do not have to) provide a free NHS sight test to you at home if you are not able to get to their premises because of ill-health or disability. Ask your optometrist if they offer this service. If you have difficulty finding someone who will visit you for a free NHS test at home, contact NHS Direct for help.

Most advice suggests that you should have your sight tested every two years. If you have diabetes, your doctor or optometrist may recommend that you have a sight test every year. Recently, the Department of Health suggested that people over the age of 70 should also have their eyes tested on the NHS every 12 months. If you are not sure how often you should visit, ask the optometrist when you next have your test.

At the end of the test, the optometrist will give you a 'prescription'. This describes what you might need in the way of glasses (spectacles) or contact lenses. You can take this prescription and use it to buy glasses or contact lenses at any opticians – you do not have to use it where you had your sight test. This prescription is free but it is not like a medicines prescription: you may still have to pay for your glasses – but see page 94, as you may be eligible for help with these costs.

## Getting glasses or contact lenses

If your sight test indicates that you need glasses or contact lenses, you may be eligible for some help with the cost if you are on a low income (see page 96). Two leaflets produced by the Department of Health help explain this system: leaflet HC11 explains about optical vouchers and it says who is entitled to help with health costs; leaflet HC12 has information on the current value of optical vouchers. If you need complex lenses, you may also be able to get help with the cost, whatever your income.

There are some types of glasses you can buy 'over the counter'. These are ready-made reading glasses that are designed to correct presbyopia (see above). They can be sold by anyone – you don't have to buy them from an ophthalmic or dispensing optician (see Box 10). But they are limited in two ways: firstly, there is a maximum prescription (or 'strength') of +4 Dioptres in each lens and, secondly, the right and left lenses will be identical.

## Other support

If, during your sight test, the optometrist finds problems that may not be solved by your having glasses or contact lenses, he or she may do one of two things:

- If your eyesight is impaired (eg your field of vision is affected so that you cannot see very much around you), the optometrist may suggest that you contact social services to find out if there is help they can give you. The optometrist may give you a form that you complete and send to your local social services department. If you are visually impaired (partially sighted) or blind (including being registered blind) you may be entitled to a range of other support, including low-vision aids.
- If there are other problems, the optometrist can refer you to a consultant ophthalmologist (a doctor specialising in eyes) at a hospital eye clinic. This might be because you have cataracts, or a weeping eye, or some other problem that may require further attention and possible treatment.

Many people who experience a sudden and major loss of vision go to an optometrist rather than their GP. The optometrist can refer you as an emergency to the hospital eye clinic. If this happens, he or she may also give you a form, LVI 2003. This is for you to use to get in touch with social services. It also contains information about other sources of advice and support.

It is up to you whether you use this form. If you do send it to social services, someone from that department will get in touch with you to see what help they can provide.

If you decide not to send the form to social services but are referred to the hospital eye clinic, you may find that clinic staff also ask if they may refer you to social services, for a social care assessment. Again, it is up to you whether or not to accept this. If you agree, the hospital clinic will send social services a form called RVI 2003.

Social services may be able to help you with information about community services for people whose vision is impaired, emotional support, practical advice and rehabilitation training (you may be eligible for a Blue Badge, for example, which would entitle someone driving you in their car to park in a disabled parking bay). Exactly what is on offer from social services will depend on the criteria your local department has set.

---

For more information, see Age Concern Factsheet 41 *Local authority assessment for community care services* and Factsheet 32 *Disability and ageing: your rights to social services.*

---

Your sight loss may mean that you are no longer able to drive – your optometrist, hospital consultant or GP will be able to advise you. You may need to contact the Driver and Vehicle Licensing Agency (DVLA), which issues driving licences, to tell them about your changed eyesight.

If you have lost some or all of your vision, you may be considered to have a disability. As a result, you might be able to get other support, such as:

- a reduced-cost BBC (TV) licence;
- disability-related benefits.

---

To find out more, see Age Concern Factsheet 3 *Television licence concessions* and Factsheet 34 *Attendance Allowance and Disability Living Allowance.*

---

In terms of NHS services, you have the right to receive information on your treatment options, as well as information (eg leaflets) meant for any member of the general public, in Braille, large print or audio, for example (as needed).

For some years the NHS and private health providers have had to make 'reasonable adjustments' to remove physical barriers to your receiving services, under the Disability Discrimination Act 1995. Since October 2004 this has included making sure there are no physical barriers to their premises that stop or make it unreasonably difficult for you to use the service. This means removing, altering or avoiding a physical feature, or providing the service in a different way.

This also applies to other services, goods and facilities available to the general public. It means not being discriminated against by your being unable to use restaurants and shops, for example. This might happen if you cannot read the price labels or menus because of your sight difficulties. Restaurants and shops can comply with the Act by making this information available to you in large print or Braille, or by having one of their staff read these out loud to you.

Voluntary organisations may be able to offer support. For example, the Guide Dogs for the Blind Association (contact details on page 274) may be able to suggest options ranging from helping you to learn to use a long-handled (or 'white') cane to your having a guide dog.

If you have a guide dog and need to use a taxi, you have a right to expect licensed taxi cabs (black cabs) to accept you as a fare under the Disability Discrimination Act 1995. There are plans for this to be extended to cover private hire taxis (minicabs). You can find out more about the Disability Discrimination Act and what it means by contacting the Disability Rights Commission (DRC; address on page 272):

Other charities, such as the Royal National Institute of the Blind (RNIB; contact details on page 281) offer goods and services, such as their Talking Books service.

## Screening for people with diabetes

The Diabetes National Service Framework (NSF) promises that, by 2007, every Primary Care Trust will offer eye-screening services to people with diabetes. The NHS has been given a target to offer screening for diabetic retinopathy to at least 80% of people with diabetes by 2006; and for everyone with diabetes to have a right to this by 2007. If you have diabetes and want to find out about arrangements for this in your area, contact your local Primary Care Trust.

# Hospital eye services

One of the most common reasons for an older person to be referred to the hospital eye service is that they have a cataract that needs removing. The target for cataract treatment is that people should not have to wait more than three months from being referred to receiving the treatment.

In some areas, there are specialist NHS eye hospitals. In other areas, eye services are part of general hospitals. In some parts of England, Primary Care Trusts have begun to contract with new Diagnostic and Treatment Centres (DTCs) to provide cataract surgery and after-care on behalf of the Primary Care Trust for NHS patients. Diagnostic and Treatment Centres are often run by private companies. As such, they have to be registered and inspected by the Healthcare Commission.

## Other private treatments

Some treatments, such as laser eye surgery to correct short sight, are rarely if ever available on the NHS. If you want this type of surgery, you need to find a private clinic that will carry this out.

Make sure you understand what the procedure involves and how much it will cost. You can always ask the advice of your GP or optometrist if you are unsure about this type of treatment. Costs vary, but remember that the price you are quoted may be only for one eye. If both eyes need treating, make sure that you know in advance what this will cost.

# Chapter 6

# Hearing services

This chapter looks at your rights to support from the NHS in terms of hearing tests, equipment and paying for hearing aids – and also considers these issues in respect of private hearing services. It tells you whom to contact to find out about entitlements to other equipment and support in the event of hearing loss or deafness – such as 'hearing dogs', British Sign Language and Typetalk.

## Introduction

The overall health of our ears can affect both our hearing and our balance. As with many other health issues, some people will reach older age with an existing hearing impairment or loss. For others, the quality of their hearing will only begin to reduce during older age. Different terms are sometimes used to describe people with hearing difficulties – these include deaf, deafened, hard of hearing, sensory impairment or sensory loss (the last two terms are also sometimes used to describe people who have lost some or all of their eyesight).

Both loss of hearing and deafness are classed as disabilities – which means that the Disability Discrimination Act 1995 applies to you (see page 68). If your hearing is impaired, you may be eligible for disability-related benefits and other support.

Further information can be found in Age Concern Factsheet 34 *Attendance Allowance and Disability Living Allowance* and Factsheet 32 *Disability and ageing: your rights to social services.*

# Losing hearing

Many people who first begin to lose some of their hearing in older age do so because of a condition called *presbyacusis*. As we grow older, the specialised cells in the innermost part of our ears (the cochlea) start to die. Sounds become less clear to us as a result. Common signs that you may be losing some of your hearing include:

- Hearing people talk – but thinking they are mumbling because you cannot make out what they are saying.
- Needing people to repeat things to you several times before you understand what they're saying.
- Needing to have your TV or radio on much louder than is needed by other people in the same room.
- Finding it difficult to follow conversations when you are in a group of people, or in a noisy environment such as a pub or café.
- Finding it difficult to hear what people say to you on the telephone.

# Diagnosis

If your hearing has changed in any way, the first thing to do is see your GP. They will begin by looking in your ears using an instrument called an otoscope. They may want to check to see if a build-up of wax in your ear is causing the problem. If so, they can arrange for you to have your ears syringed. This is usually done by a nurse based at the surgery.

Your GP may carry out some other tests. These can involve using a tuning fork (used to tune musical instruments to particular notes) to find out a bit more about the type of problem you are experiencing, or they may test your hearing in other ways. If there is a problem, the GP will probably want to refer you to specialist hearing services – either the ear, nose and throat (ENT) department of a hospital or the audiology department (or audiology clinic) in a hospital.

If you are referred to the ENT department, that department will get in touch to make an appointment for you to see an ENT consultant (the specialist doctor). Chapter 11 describes how soon you should be seen after you have been referred. The consultant will probably ask you whether there is any family history of deafness and may do some tests. Depending on the reasons for your hearing loss, he or she may then refer you in turn to the audiology department.

If you are over the age of 60, the chances are that your GP will refer you straight away to the audiology department rather than get you to see the ENT consultant first. This is because the audiology department tends to be the most appropriate part of the NHS to deal with hearing loss for most older people. In this case, avoiding having to go to the ENT department first helps to speed things up for you. But if you are worried about this, ask your GP to explain.

## Audiology tests

The audiologist (the professional working in the audiology department or clinic) tests your hearing using an audiometer. This is a piece of equipment that produces a range of sounds and you will be asked to say which of them you can hear. The audiologist uses these results to see if a hearing aid would help you. There is a wide range of hearing aids available, both on the NHS and privately. They will improve your hearing – but your hearing will not be fully restored.

# NHS hearing aids

NHS hearing aids are provided free of charge. In England since April 2005, this has included digital hearing aids for new patients. These digital aids look similar to the older, analogue hearing aids that people wear but the Royal National Institute for Deaf People (RNID) says they give a better sound quality. One of the reasons is that it is possible to modify a digital hearing aid very precisely, to give a very good 'fit' with your particular hearing difficulties. They are also often designed to reduce steady background noise (eg traffic noise). This can make it more comfortable for you to concentrate on your conversation. They can also be programmed for different environments – for example, to suit someone whether they are at home watching the TV or out shopping in a busy supermarket.

If you already have an analogue hearing aid, there will probably be a wait before you are reassessed for a digital aid, using criteria set by your Primary Care Trust.

Do bear in mind that digital hearing aids are not suitable for everyone's hearing problem. An analogue hearing aid may be a better option for you.

When you see the audiologist, ask how soon you will receive your hearing aid. Once it has been fitted, you may need to go back to the clinic after a few weeks for adjustments to the aid.

# Private hearing tests and aids

You can also choose to pay for a private hearing test, and buy a hearing aid from a private hearing aid dispenser. They often have shops in the high street, or you can find their details in your local telephone directory. You might decide to 'go private' if you want a hearing aid fitted very quickly, or there is a particular design you want that isn't available on the NHS. Private hearing tests cost around £25. If you find somewhere that doesn't charge, be aware that this may mean you are not given a copy of the results of your hearing test (an audiogram). You will need a copy of your audiogram if you decide to buy a hearing aid from a different dispenser from the one who carried out the test.

If you are thinking about buying a hearing aid privately, it is still worth seeing your GP first. They can advise whether further medical tests are needed. Your GP may also be able to give you information about hearing-aid dispensers in your area.

Sometimes private hearing-aid dispensers have a base in an NHS hospital; or you might want to arrange to see the NHS audiologist privately if he or she has a private practice. A private hearing aid can cost anything from £300 to £2,500. They may last for up to five years – but you will need to buy another aid when your current one fails. If you have private medical insurance, make sure that this policy covers the cost of hearing aids before ordering the device.

The RNID (contact details on page 281) advises you not to respond to advertisements in newspapers or on television or radio offering free or cheap hearing devices. This is because you may find you are on the receiving end of high-pressure sales tactics; at present you won't have as many rights as a consumer if you contact the company and they visit you at home at your invitation (there are proposals to tighten up this area of consumer law in the future).

---

The RNID produces a factsheet about hearing aids – *All About Hearing Aids* – that you may find helpful.

---

# Tinnitus

Tinnitus is a common hearing problem that can happen at any age. It is the condition where people hear noises in their ears or in their heads – noises such as ringing, whistling or buzzing.

Equipment known as sound or noise generators can be useful for someone with tinnitus. They work by helping to mask the noise you hear – for example, by producing a 'shhh' or soothing noise. Some devices can be fitted in your ear; others attach to a hearing aid. They are available free as part of NHS tinnitus treatment in hospital. Ask your GP or consultant about this.

They can also be bought privately from hearing-aid dispensers but they can be expensive. Try to find a dispenser who will offer you a trial period of at least 30 days. That way you can test it out in as wide a range of settings as possible to make sure it will be of some benefit.

The RNID runs a specialist helpline for people with tinnitus.

# Hearing dogs

As with guide dogs for people with sight loss, hearing dogs are provided by charities. The main charity involved is Hearing Dogs for the Deaf. The dogs help people with no or little hearing by touching the person with a paw to alert them to household sounds such as telephone, doorbell and alarm clock as well as public fire alarms and bomb alerts.

It is up to the charity concerned whether you would be suited to a hearing dog. If you have a hearing dog, under the Disability Discrimination Act 1995 you should be able to take it with you into hotels, restaurants and shops – just as with a guide dog for a blind person. There may be some exceptions, though, if there is a good reason why a dog should not be accepted – such as areas where food is being prepared.

For further information, contact Hearing Dogs for Deaf People (details on page 275).

You may also want to contact the charity the British Deaf Association (BDA; details on page 267) to find out about the services they offer to deaf people.

## British Sign Language

There are various courses available to people who would like to learn to 'speak' British Sign Language (BSL). Your local education authority (LEA) may run day or evening classes. Social services may be involved with running BSL classes for people who have recently lost some or all of their hearing. There may also be lip-reading courses available. Contact your local council. RNID may also have further suggestions.

## Typetalk

Typetalk is a service that supports people with hearing or speech difficulties to communicate with hearing people. It is run by the Royal National Institute for Deaf People (RNID) and funded by British Telecom (BT).

People with hearing or speech problems can use a special telephone – a textphone – to 'talk' to other people and organisations. Typetalk provides a link between the two – a Typetalk operator. The operator reads out loud to the hearing person the words typed by the textphone user. As the hearing person replies, the Typetalk operator types what is said for the user to read the response on the textphone display panel.

To find out more about Typetalk and how to join, free, contact RNID Typetalk (details under Royal National Institute for Deaf People, page 281).

Some older people also find that sending and receiving text messages via a mobile telephone, or using email, are useful ways of communicating with both hearing and hearing-impaired people.

## Cochlear implants

A cochlear implant is a device for people with severe to profound deafness, for whom hearing aids do not help. It involves an operation to the middle ear, under general anaesthetic, carried out in a hospital ENT department. The implant system stimulates the auditory nerve, and helps people to gain awareness of environmental sounds, understand speech without lip-reading and perhaps to use the telephone. Whether a cochlear implant is right for you is up to your consultant. You may also want to contact the charity, National Cochlear Implant Users Association (NCIUA; address on page 279), if you have or think you should have an implant.

## Chapter 7

# Therapists, and other support

This chapter looks at a broad range of support from therapists, including physiotherapists, occupational therapists (OTs), music and arts therapists, and speech and language therapists. It describes how to access this type of support through the NHS, and whom else to approach.

It also explores buying these services privately, as well as looking at three aspects of the National Service Framework (NSF) for Older People:

- falls clinics and services;
- stroke services;
- intermediate care.

Other types of support, such as wigs and wheelchairs from the NHS and help with costs, are also explored in this chapter.

Support for people with mental ill-health or distress is included in Chapter 8; bereavement counselling is discussed in Chapter 15.

## Types of therapy

There are lots of different types of therapy services provided by a range of therapists. We tend to think about therapeutic support in one of two ways:

- for physical ailments and problems – for example, physiotherapy, or speech and language therapy;
- to support people with mental ill-health (such as counselling services, and art therapy).

Many types of therapy cross over these two aspects. For example, helping someone with the practical skills of everyday life, such as being able to lift your arm to brush your hair after having had a stroke, can be very effective in improving how you feel about yourself and your life as well as helping you regain physical abilities.

Most therapists need to be registered with the Health Professions Council (HPC). These are:

- occupational therapists;
- speech and language therapists;
- art, music and drama therapists;
- physiotherapists.

People who are not registered are not allowed to use these professional titles. To do so would be a criminal offence, for which they could be prosecuted. Registration under the Health Professions Council is a relatively recent requirement and replaces the previous state registration scheme. As a result, few therapists now use the term 'state registered' – so don't be concerned if the title of the therapist you see does not include those words. The important point to establish is that they are registered with the Health Professions Council (see page 241).

## Occupational therapists (OTs)

The College of Occupational Therapists describes the role of OTs as enabling people to achieve health, well-being and life satisfaction through taking part in occupation. The type of 'occupation' varies from person to person but covers the usual daily tasks and activities that meet our need to look after ourselves and enjoy taking part in society.

In broad terms, there are three main ways that occupational therapists (OTs) work with older people:

■ Advising people on how to manage on a practical basis in their own home; this can include using the stairs, lifting pots and pans in order to cook, or advice about having grab rails or a stairlift fitted.

■ Helping people to look after themselves physically, such as re-learning how to wash their hair or to cook. (There is more about this later in the sections 'Intermediate care' and 'Stroke services'.)

■ Giving support to people with mental health difficulties, helping them to take part in different hobbies and leisure interests or through reminiscence sessions (see also Chapter 8).

OTs can be employed either by the NHS or by the local authority social services department. Those with social services departments are often involved in work to adapt the homes of people with physical disabilities or ill-health to help them to continue living there for as long as possible. Such adaptations are often paid for through a means-tested system. This means you might be asked to pay something towards the cost of the work, based on your income and savings. There are several different systems, explained in the Age Concern Factsheet listed below. But if you are advised by an OT employed either by your local council or by the NHS that an adaptation will cost less than £1,000, this will be carried out free of charge. The advice from OTs is also free.

To find out more about help with housing adaptations, you can:

■ Read Age Concern Factsheet 13 *Older home owners: financial help with repairs and adaptations.*

■ Contact your local Home Improvement Agency – sometimes called Care & Repair or Staying Put scheme (often run by a voluntary organisation but sometimes by a department in your local council).

■ Contact your local council's housing department.

OTs employed by NHS hospitals can advise you on whether you can safely leave hospital, or whether some adaptations might be needed at home before your return. They might also advise about equipment needed to help you, on either a temporary or a permanent basis. For example:

■ a walking stick or frame;
■ a wheelchair;
■ hand-held items to help you to put on your shoes or to pull up stockings, tights or socks.

Equipment stores providing this type of support are run jointly by the NHS and local social services departments (see page 99).

---

**Box 11. Getting to see an OT**

Your route to an OT depends on the sort of help you are looking for.

If you want advice on adaptations to your home, this is most likely to be via your local council. You won't be asked to pay for the OT's visits or advice if they are employed by the council but in some areas there are long delays getting to see an OT this way. This has been a problem for some years, due largely to a shortage of qualified OTs willing to take on these roles. As a result, some local councils have begun to use occupational therapy assistants (OTAs) to advise people on more routine adaptations, such as handrails. They may also set up contracts with a voluntary organisation to provide and

---

fix the rail, if this is needed, through Handyperson or similar schemes. Your local Age Concern should be able to tell you about arrangements in your area.

Older people with mental health problems are most likely to see an OT via their GP. They may do so as part of attending an NHS day hospital (see Chapter 8).

Advice from an NHS-hospital OT will probably be sought on your behalf by the consultant in charge of your care. This could involve you and the OT going to your home on a short visit, to make sure that you will be able to manage things when you are discharged from hospital. If no one suggests you should see an OT while you are in hospital, ask your consultant or the ward sister if this can be arranged, explaining why you think this is needed. (There is more information about coming out of hospital in Chapter 12.)

As with many services, there must be an appropriate reason for you to see an OT. Although you have the right *to ask* to see an OT, this does not mean that you will see one.

## Private OTs

There may be some OTs working privately in your area. If you decide to see a private OT, you will have to pay them: make sure you know before your visit how much this will be. Remember that, to be able lawfully to call him- or herself an OT, the person must be registered as such with the Health Professions Council.

Bear in mind that, even if you see an OT privately for advice about housing adaptations, if you need to apply for a grant to pay for the work, it may still be necessary for the council's own OT to visit you –

so this won't necessarily speed things up for you. It's also very unlikely that you'll be able to claim the cost of seeing an OT privately (for this or other reasons) from either the NHS or your council.

# Art, music and drama therapy

Art, music and drama therapists should be registered under the Health Professions Council, regardless of whether they are employed by the NHS or run their own private practices or work within charities. Registered professionals can also use the term 'art psychotherapist'.

These three therapies use different approaches to encourage people to express their feelings and emotions through music or drama or art such as drawing and painting. Each therapy has its own separate training.

Although there are art therapists, music therapists and drama therapists employed in the NHS, provision of this kind of support is quite patchy across England. You need to be referred by either your GP or a consultant. Some charities offer these therapies to older people who already receive other services from them. For example, some charities that run nursing homes for older people with profound levels of dementia or other mental disability or ill-health may offer regular music therapy sessions to their residents. But deciding to do this is up to the charity concerned. (For more information, see also Chapters 8 and 13.)

# Speech and language therapists

Speech and language therapists (SLTs) specialise in communication disorders or difficulties. These disorders might arise because of a stroke, for example, or a head injury or difficulties such as:

- Parkinson's disease, multiple sclerosis (MS), motor neurone disease (MND), dementia;

- cancer of the head, neck or throat;
- mental health difficulties;
- stammering;
- hearing problems.

Speech and language therapists diagnose and assess speech and language problems, and work with people to increase their communication abilities to the maximum possible. They also work with people who have difficulties in swallowing and eating and drinking. This can particularly affect people who have had a stroke (see also 'Stroke services', page 90).

Speech and language therapists often work for the NHS in hospitals, running in-patient and out-patient services. They can also provide NHS support in community settings, such as health centres or people's own homes. It very much depends on the individual's need, and on local arrangements.

Speech and language therapists are often also involved with intermediate care services, alongside OTs. You will see an NHS speech and language therapist by being referred to them:

- by your GP;
- by a hospital consultant;
- through the local intermediate care arrangements.

Professional speech and language therapists must be registered with the Health Professions Council.

Some speech and language therapists work privately. As with other services, if you arrange this privately you must be prepared to pay the amount set by the therapist. There is no 'national rate' for private therapy, so the amount can vary from one professional to another.

# Physiotherapy

Physiotherapists (physios) use a range of techniques to restore or improve movement of the body. They treat common problems such as back pain and muscle sprain but can also help people to deal with incontinence, osteoporosis and depression.

Your GP is the person most likely to refer you to an NHS physiotherapist if he or she thinks this is necessary. Again, you have the right to ask for a referral.

Physiotherapists can run their own private practices and clinics – again, you would have to pay for treatment you arrange privately. Physiotherapists must also register with the Health Professions Council.

---

**Box 12. Paying privately**

If you are paying privately and have a private medical insurance scheme, or a 'cash back' treatment plan, check whether this covers contributions towards physiotherapy or any of the other therapies discussed in this chapter. If so, you may be able to use these sums towards the costs of buying this support privately.

---

# Falls clinics

The NHS has to provide 'falls clinics', under Standard Six of the National Service Framework (NSF) for Older People. The two main aims in this standard are:

- to reduce the number of falls that result in serious injury;
- to make sure that anyone who does fall receives effective treatment and rehabilitation.

Falls in older age are a major cause of disability. They also result in a large number of deaths each year among older people. Injuries from falls, such as a fractured hip, can seriously reduce an individual's independence and, in some cases, may result in their having to move into a care home far sooner than if they had not fallen. Reducing the number of falls, and of injuries from falls, has been a major government target for some years.

People fall for lots of reasons, including:

■ poor eyesight (see Chapter 5);
■ rushing to the toilet because of incontinence (see Chapter 3);
■ dementia (see Chapter 8);
■ loss of leg (muscle) strength and ability to balance;
■ side effects of some medication.

From April 2005, every Primary Care Trust must have a falls service across local health and social care systems (sometimes called an 'integrated service'). This is provided free of charge to you. The actual services provided may vary from area to area but they typically offer two things. The first is support to help prevent falls. This might include:

■ Exercise classes to help people improve their balance and strength.
■ Advice from chiropodists on suitable footwear.
■ Information packs.
■ Talks and demonstrations on how to reduce your risk of falling at home and when out and about.

The second element of a falls service is to provide support for people who have already fallen and, because of the increased risk, may fall again. Examples include providing hip protectors (these go over the top of underwear and look a little like very padded pants) for older people most at risk of falls (such as those living in care homes offering nursing) and specialist hospital services where people receive intensive occupational and physiotherapy support following surgery on fractured hips (fractured neck of femur). You may find that these are not provided free of charge; in November 2004 the National Institute for Health and Clinical Excellence (NICE) decided not to recommend that the NHS provide hip protectors because of insufficient evidence of the benefit of these items.

The criteria for deciding who can have this support are set by each Primary Care Trust, depending how it judges what should be organised locally in order to meet the national target of reducing falls. For example, in one area, older people who have attended the local hospital A&E department because of a fall are referred by hospital staff to their local falls prevention service. In another area, older people who have fallen in the last year can refer themselves to a local falls clinic so that they can be assessed on the risk that they might fall again, and receive support and advice as needed. Your Primary Care Trust may offer something quite different.

---

To find out more about falls services in your area:

- ask your GP (Chapter 3);
- contact NHS Direct (Chapter 2);
- contact your local Patient Advice and Liaison Service (PALS) at the Primary Care Trust (PCT);
- ask your local Age Concern (you can find it by looking in your telephone book, searching on Age Concern's website or telephoning Age Concern's Information Line – contact details on page 264).

There are two other charities you can contact for more information. Help the Aged (page 276) has a range of leaflets and other information about preventing falls. The National Osteoporosis Society (page 280) also has a variety of advice and information available on osteoporosis, one of the particular risk elements for falling.

---

# Intermediate care

'Intermediate care' is a term used to describe services that provide a structured, time-limited period of rehabilitation to help people recover as much independence as possible. Typically, this offers you a 'bridge' of support between your being in hospital and going home or moving to a care home. Intermediate care has to be provided under Standard Three of the National Service Framework for Older People. The aim is to:

- provide integrated services to promote faster recovery from illness;
- prevent unnecessary hospital admissions;
- support timely discharge from hospital;
- maximise independent living;
- prevent premature or unnecessary admission to long-term residential care.

In recent years, the NHS and local councils have been given money to invest in intermediate care services. But they are not available for everyone – to be eligible, you have to meet the local criteria.

Intermediate care includes services provided to people in their own homes as well as 'intermediate care beds' (some in hospital, others in care homes or sheltered housing schemes). Typically, intermediate care provides intensive occupational therapy, physiotherapy, speech and language therapy, and other practical support and advice – including rebuilding people's confidence. It is given for a maximum of six weeks for each person, and is free. By March 2004, and compared with figures for 1999/2000 across England, this was to mean at least:

- an extra 5,000 intermediate care beds;
- an additional 1,700 non-residential intermediate care places;

- 150,000 additional people receiving intermediate care services to promote rehabilitation and 'supported discharge' (discharge from either a hospital ward or a hospital Accident & Emergency (A&E) department);
- 70,000 additional people receiving intermediate care support to prevent unnecessary admission to hospital.

These figures are the totals for the whole of England, not for each individual Primary Care Trust area.

Details of what has been achieved are expected in a national report from the Healthcare Commission, the Commission for Social Care Inspection and the Audit Commission in December 2005.

Local arrangements for accessing intermediate care services vary. This means you could be referred to it by your GP, by a hospital consultant or another NHS professional or by someone working for social services – perhaps a social worker or care manager. Most people are referred following a stay in hospital or arrival at a hospital A&E department after a fall or other emergency. Intermediate care services have tended to focus on people's physical needs and home environment; there are plans also to look at mental health issues as well.

## Stroke services

Standard Five of the National Service Framework for Older People aims to reduce the number of people who have a stroke and to make sure that those who *have* had a stroke have prompt access to integrated stroke care services. This means that people who are thought to have had a stroke:

- can get this diagnosed, using any necessary equipment such as a CT scan;
- are treated appropriately by a specialist stroke service;

■ subsequently take part in a multi-disciplinary programme of secondary prevention and rehabilitation (with any unpaid, informal or family carers).

Since April 2004, you have the right to expect that every GP practice:

■ is identifying and treating patients who are at risk of having a stroke;

■ follows the local agreements for the rapid referral and management of the care of people with transient ischaemic attack (TIA, a sort of mini-stroke);

■ has identified patients who have had a stroke and is treating them in line with local agreements;

■ has established 'clinical audit systems' for stroke, to identify any patterns in stroke patients and their treatment needs.

In broad terms, the 'local agreement' means what the specialist stroke services and GPs in an area have agreed to do for patients in primary care.

You also have the right to expect every NHS general hospital caring for people with stroke to have a specialised stroke service, and to be referred to this if you are admitted to hospital following a stroke or have a stroke while in hospital. (See also Chapter 11.)

# Complaints

Any complaint about the NHS – whether about a service it provides or because it's not providing a service you think is needed – can be made through the NHS complaints system. You can also complain about individual NHS staff through this route. This is explained in Chapter 16.

## Other support

As well as help from therapists, the NHS provides a range of other support.

## Wigs and support stockings

The NHS provides wigs and fabric supports to some patients. 'Fabric supports' means something that helps to support your spine or abdomen, or an item such as a surgical bra.

The NHS provides these free if you are in hospital as an in-patient. If you are an out-patient (going to an NHS clinic for appointments), you may be asked to pay a prescription charge for these items. In this case, you may be entitled to reduced charge or a free item, depending on your income. There is no charge if you are exempt because you receive a war pension.

There is more about help with these costs in the free leaflet HC11 *Help with health costs*, published by the Department of Health. You can get copies at a post office, or from the staff at the hospital or clinic. See also page 270.

## Help with NHS charges

Although many NHS services are free to people aged 60 or over, there are some charges that apply to:

- dentistry;
- spectacles and contact lenses;
- travel to and from hospital;
- wigs and other 'support' items.

If you are on a low income, you may be eligible to pay reduced charges for these services. The Department of Health has a freephone advice line, giving information on NHS charges (see page 270).

# NHS dentistry

You do not have to pay for NHS dental treatment if you or your partner (someone of the opposite sex whom you are married to, or live with as if married) receives:

- Pension Credit, guarantee credit; *or*
- Pension Credit, guarantee credit with savings credit.

The Pension Credit is a system of state financial support for people over the state pension age. Whether you qualify depends on your income from all sources (including your state pension) plus any savings you have. You are not eligible for exemption from NHS dental charges if you are over the age of 65 and receive only the savings credit element of Pension Credit (that is, you do not also get the guarantee credit element) but you may still be able to claim some help on the grounds of low income – see 'NHS Low Income Scheme', on page 96.

---

**Pension Credit is explained in detail in Age Concern Factsheet 48** *Pension Credit*.

---

Anyone under the age of 60 who receives Income Support (IS) or income-based Jobseekers Allowance (JSA IB) is entitled to free NHS dental treatment.

If you qualify for free dental care through any of these routes, show the surgery (either the receptionist or the dentist) your 'award notice' each time you start a new course of NHS treatment. Your award notice is the letter you received from either the Pension Service or the JobCentre Plus office, saying that you receive the relevant benefit.

Even if you do not receive any type of Pension Credit help, you may still be eligible for some help with dental costs on the grounds of low income, via the NHS Low Income Scheme (see page 96). As well as being eligible on the grounds of low income, you may qualify for help if you receive a war disablement pension and you need dental treatment because of the disability for which that pension was awarded.

## Help with the costs of glasses and contact lenses

If you receive the 'guarantee credit' component of Pension Credit, you will be eligible for vouchers towards the cost of glasses or contact lenses, if it is decided you need these following your NHS eye test.

The optometrist who carried out the NHS eye test will write a prescription that shows the type of lenses you will need. You can take a copy of this prescription away with you.

If you are eligible for help towards the cost of glasses, the optometrist will also give you an optical voucher. If you need a pair of glasses for reading and another for distance, you will be given two vouchers.

The value of the voucher varies depending on the type of lenses you need. The stronger the lenses, the more the voucher will be worth. Vouchers can be used towards the cost of single-vision, bifocal, varifocal or contact lenses.

If you have an HC2 certificate under the NHS Low Income Scheme (see page 96), you will be entitled to the full value of the voucher for your type of lens. However, if the glasses you want cost more than the value of the voucher, you will be expected to pay the difference yourself.

If you have an HC3 certificate, this will tell you the maximum amount you should contribute towards the cost of your glasses. For example, if the certificate says you should contribute £22 and the glasses you want cost £46.50, your voucher will give you £24.50 towards the cost of your glasses.

If you have lost or damaged your glasses or contact lenses as a result of an illness, and you have an HC2 or HC3 certificate, ask your dispensing optician if you can get help towards the cost of replacement or repair. You should note that there is no help available towards the costs of general wear and tear.

## Help with the cost of wigs and support items

As outlined on page 92, if you are an out-patient (going to an NHS clinic for appointments), you may be asked to pay a prescription charge for these items. If you have a low income, you may be entitled to pay a reduced charge or even pay nothing through the NHS Low Income Scheme – but you must apply for this help (page 96).

Even if you are not entitled to a free wig, you can still get one from the hospital at a subsidised rate. In this case, hospital staff will give you a form to give to your wig supplier to offset the cost. The procedure is explained in the Department of Health leaflet HC12 *NHS charges and optical voucher values*.

You may prefer to choose a wig from a hairdresser or wig supplier, although this can be a bit more expensive. VAT (Value Added Tax) does not have to be paid on wigs when hair loss is caused by cancer treatment. You will need to fill in a VAT form, which most shops will give you, when you buy the wig. The tax cannot be claimed back at a later date.

## Help with the costs of travel to hospital

If you are a War Pensioner, the cost of travel to an NHS hospital for treatment overseen by a consultant is free if the treatment you are having is for the condition or disability for which you receive this pension. Otherwise, you will need to apply for help through the NHS Low Income Scheme (see page 96).

If you have an HC2 or HC3 certificate, the hospital is responsible for reimbursing your relevant travel costs. You should always speak to the hospital staff before travelling if you have questions about the help you may receive.

If you need someone to travel with you for medical reasons, a doctor or other appropriate health professional will have to agree that this is the case before your companion's travel expenses will be paid.

You should aim to use the cheapest means available at the time you need to travel. The hospital decides what is necessary – this tends to be public transport, using a private car (this cost is then based on fuel used) or voluntary car schemes. Taxis are an exception, so if using a taxi is your only option, discuss this with the hospital before you travel to make sure they agree about this cost. You can also speak with hospital staff if it would be difficult for you to pay for your transport and then claim it back. They can consider sending payment in advance.

Under the NHS Low Income Scheme, the HC2 certificate will entitle you to a full refund of reasonable costs. An HC3 certificate will show how much you should contribute towards transport costs each time you need to go to the hospital.

There is no help towards the cost of travel to visit someone in hospital.

## NHS Low Income Scheme

You apply to the NHS Low Income Scheme by filling in and sending off form HC1. Your dentist or optometrist may have copies of this form, or you can obtain it from your local Pension Service office (this is your local social security office – find it in your telephone book).

For copies of leaflets, you can also telephone (free) the Department of Health's Health literature line on 0800 555 777. The leaflets to ask for are:

- HC1 *Help with health costs* – this is the claim form you will need to fill in
- HC11 *Help with health costs* – this leaflet explains whether you are eligible to claim
- HC11 (LP) – this is a large-print version of the HC11 leaflet.

If you live in a care home and receive financial support from your local social services department to pay for this, you will need to fill in a different form – HC1 (SC). If you live in a care home but pay for this in full yourself, you may be eligible for help under the NHS Low Income Scheme depending on how much savings and income you have.

The form will explain what counts as a low income; it also tells you what you need to provide in the way of information to support your claim, and where to send the form once you have filled it in. If you qualify for help, you will be sent one or other of two certificates:

- Certificate HC2, which entitles you to *full* help with costs such as NHS dental charges and optical lenses (for spectacles or contact lenses); *or*
- Certificate HC3, which entitles you to *some* help. The certificate you receive will tell you the maximum amount you will have to pay, which will also depend on the cost of the treatment. For example, if your certificate says you must pay for the first £30 of any dental treatment and the treatment costs £45, you will pay £30 and the dentist will claim the remaining £15 from the Low Income Scheme via the Primary Care Trust.

Ideally, you should apply before your current course of treatment comes to an end. But it is possible to claim for a refund for NHS charges you have paid recently – see below.

If you are aged 60 or over, your certificate usually lasts for 12 months. If you have a current certificate, take this with you when you go to the dentist, for new glasses or to hospital. Remember to apply for a new certificate – it is not renewed automatically. Do this by completing another claim form (HC1) four weeks before your current certificate comes to an end (remember that you will need a different version of the form if you are in a care home).

There is more about this system in Age Concern Information Sheet IS20 *Help with health costs for older people*.

## Refunds of NHS charges

You may be able to claim a refund for NHS charges you have paid in the past three months. You might be eligible because:

- You are on a low income – but you have not yet applied for a certificate.
- You are exempt from NHS charges but did not tell the dentist or dispensing optician at the time (perhaps because you did not realise that you were exempt).
- You did not provide proof as needed by the dental surgery, hospital or dispensing optician's (eg you did not take with you your certificate or your letter about Pension Credit).

If you have a valid certificate but left it at home, the dentist or dispending optician is entitled to ask you to pay the full relevant NHS charges there and then. This is because you must show your entitlement at the time of the treatment or when buying the spectacles, or arriving at hospital for treatment, not afterwards. In this situation, it is up to you to apply for a refund.

You make a claim for a refund on form HC5. This is available from your local post office or Pension Service office (you could also ask about it at your dentist's surgery or at the optician's).

If you do not hold a valid certificate, you will need to complete form HC5 *and* form HC1 described above. You will also need to send in your receipt from the dentist or dispensing optician – so make sure you always keep these. And you need to apply within three months of paying the charge.

## Joint Equipment Stores

Equipment is one of the areas where the NHS and local social services departments have to work closely. There will be a Joint Equipment Store in your part of England, run jointly by the local Primary Care Trust and local social services department.

You do not have to pay for any free-standing equipment from this store. Minor adaptations such as grab rails or a handrail to the stairs are also free up to a maximum cost of £1,000 (this amount includes any costs to fix equipment in place). Equipment that might be provided includes:

- pressure-relief mattress;
- commode;
- shower chair;
- raised toilet seat;
- equipment for deaf or hard-of-hearing people (eg a telephone with a flashing light).

You may have to be assessed by either an occupational therapist or a physiotherapist before you can receive equipment from the Joint Store. Equipment can also be requested by district nurses and the local continence service.

If you need help with larger adaptations to your home, such as a walk-in/wheel-in shower, you may be asked to pay towards the cost. There are various forms of financial support available from your local council (not the NHS).

---

Age Concern Factsheet 13 *Older home owners: financial help with repairs and adaptations* and Factsheet 42 *Disability equipment and how to get it* have further information.

---

If you live in a care home – particularly in a care home offering nursing care – the home will be expected to provide equipment for basic handling, lifting and mobility, and adaptations. But you have the same rights to equipment and aids as if you were still living in your own home. If you need specific items that would not be suitable for (or are not needed by) other residents, these may be provided by the local Joint Equipment Stores. You could ask the care home manager to get in touch with the equipment store on your behalf.

## Wheelchairs and walking frames

If you have a long-term need for a wheelchair, including an electrically powered wheelchair, the NHS will provide this on what is in effect a long-term loan basis. This means that the wheelchair doesn't belong to you – the NHS will expect it to be returned when it is no longer used, even if it was specially designed just for you. Your GP, or a hospital consultant, can refer you to be assessed by the local NHS service for a wheelchair. If it is agreed you should have an NHS wheelchair, the NHS will be responsible for its repairs and maintenance (provided this is not needed because the wheelchair has been misused or not looked after properly).

Sometimes, instead of the NHS providing you with a wheelchair, it will offer you wheelchair vouchers. These vouchers are worth the equivalent of a standard chair, and you can put this towards the cost of a wheelchair that costs more than the NHS will provide free of charge. You can do this through the NHS or use the voucher with a private wheelchair company.

If you need a wheelchair for a short time, the NHS may lend you one. If not, organisations such as local British Red Cross branches and Age Concerns can sometimes lend wheelchairs on a short-term basis (see pages 267 and 285 for contact details).

In some parts of the country there is a long wait for the NHS wheelchair service. If this affects you, you could contact your local Patient Advice and Liaison Service (PALS) for help. The Limbless Association also has information for people who need to use a wheelchair – see page 277 for contact details.

You may also find a Shopmobility scheme near you. The schemes lend manual and powered wheelchairs, and powered scooters, to people who need these in order to be mobile around their town.

To get walking aids such as a frame or a stick from the NHS you will first be assessed by a physiotherapist (see page 86). As well as assessing what you need, the physiotherapist will be able to show you how to use the equipment safely.

---

Age Concern Factsheet 42 *Disability equipment and how to use it* has more details.

---

# Chapter 8

# Mental health

This chapter considers commonly experienced mental ill-health –
permanent, temporary and fluctuating conditions such as
dementia, depression and schizophrenia. It looks at how a
diagnosis is made, your rights to drug treatments, access to
support, compulsory treatments and after-care services. It also
describes decision-making in situations when a person lacks the
'mental capacity' to decide for him- or herself, and safeguards for
someone who is detained in hospital.

Some people find the phrase 'mental health' a difficult one to use.
This may be because of concerns about the stigma that can be
attached to these types of illnesses and disabilities. Others feel
that the word 'mental' is too often used as an insult or that it
applies only to the tiny number of people in the UK who might
behave violently as a result of their illness. But within the NHS
'mental health' is used widely to describe services and support for
people with all these types of illnesses and disabilities.

## Mental ill-health

There is a wide range of types of mental ill-health. Those most
commonly connected with older age include dementia and
depression. But many people under the age of 60 are also depressed,

and some may develop particular types of dementia at younger ages. Schizophrenia, for example, tends to develop in younger people but in some people it does not appear until older age.

Mental health problems can be:

■ temporary, *or*

■ permanent, *or*

■ fluctuating.

An example of a temporary problem might be anxiety caused as a side effect of medication. A permanent problem could include dementia. Depression is an example of a condition that may fluctuate – that is, it may change from one day to the next.

Three of the more familiar mental health problems – dementia, depression and schizophrenia – are explored below. But there are many other examples of poor mental health:

■ alcoholism

■ anxiety

■ delusions.

## Depression

The term 'depression' is often used to describe a huge range of feelings, from feeling low to having a severe problem that interferes with everyday life. But depression is not the same thing as being unhappy. People with severe depression may experience very low moods and loss of any interest and pleasure in life, as well as feeling worthless or guilty.

Although depression can affect anyone, older people are more likely to be affected than any other age group. There are many reasons for this, including being widowed or divorced, increased physical difficulties, feeling isolated, side effects from medication, and neurobiological (the workings of the brain) changes to do with getting older. Even retiring from paid work can, for some people, trigger a period of depression.

## Diagnosis

As with any illness, getting a diagnosis is the first step. It can be difficult to diagnose depression if it occurs alongside other illnesses and disabilities such as dementia (see below), stroke, cancer or other physical problems. But this doesn't mean it should go undetected. If you (or someone you know) are becoming withdrawn or feel very unhappy, lack energy or have lost interest in everyday life, or are experiencing some other change in your behaviour or attitude towards life, this should all be explained in a visit to the GP.

If you are feeling desperate to the point of thinking about suicide and want help, it is really important that you explain how badly you are feeling. You could:

- Telephone NHS Direct – if needed, they will call an ambulance for you, to take you to hospital.
- Telephone your GP, or go to the surgery – explain how you are feeling and ask to speak to a doctor straight away. If you do not feel well enough to get to the surgery, telephone and ask for a doctor to visit you at home as a matter of urgency.
- Telephone the emergency services on 999, tell them how you feel and ask for an ambulance.
- Go to the nearest hospital A&E department.

If you don't want any help from the NHS at this time, you could contact the charity Samaritans. They will talk to you in confidence, which means what you say stays private, and you won't have to tell them your name or where you live, if you don't want to.

The Samaritans also have over 200 local groups, many of which are open to visitors who need to talk to someone in person. You don't need to be feeling suicidal to contact Samaritans. They can offer support to people in many different circumstances. You can also write to the Samaritans if you are in a crisis and need to write about how this feels. If you give a return address, your letter will be answered. And you can get in touch with them by email. (See page 282 for contact details.)

There are other organisations offering support to people with mental ill-health. For example, the Mental Health Foundation has several factsheets about different mental illnesses, including depression. You may also want to contact the organisation Depression Alliance, which offers information and advice for people with depression, amongst other support. (Contact details are on pages 278 and 271.)

## Treatment and support

There are lots of different approaches that can help with depression but they won't all help everyone. Even though one of the difficulties for someone with depression is that it can be very hard to find the energy or interest to try different options, it is worth persevering to find what will help you. For some people this will be medication (perhaps antidepressants; in 2004, the National Institute for Health and Clinical Excellence issued guidance on the use of some antidepressants as a treatment for depression), whilst for others it will be a combination of changes to their diet, physical exercise (such as a regular walk or yoga exercises) and having something to do – perhaps activities organised by an occupational therapist, if the depression is more severe (see below).

Some people find what are often called 'the talking therapies' very helpful. These include particular approaches such as cognitive behavioural therapy (CBT). This involves your seeing a counsellor trained to use techniques to help you learn about and change your approach to situations in your life. Usually, you meet with the counsellor for fixed appointments, perhaps for half an hour or an hour each time, once a week for a period of several weeks. Sometimes CBT sessions (or other therapeutic approaches) are available on the NHS – ask your GP what is available locally and whether this would be helpful for you. Chapter 15 has information about counselling for people who have been bereaved.

You could also look into paying privately for therapy (Box 13).

---

**Box 13. Private therapy**

There are many different approaches to psychological therapy, sometimes also called psychotherapy. You need to find the one that you feel is most suited to you. You should also find a counsellor or psychotherapist you feel comfortable with. Counsellors and therapists should be able to give you some information about the approach they use. You can always book one session to start with, to get a feel for the approach and the person. A good counsellor will understand if, after this first session, you decide that their style or their approach is not right for you.

First sessions often last for longer than subsequent, or later, sessions. This is because the therapist needs to start by hearing from you the reasons why you have come to see them. If there is a lot to explain, this may take some time. It's not unusual for a first session to be one hour, or an hour and a half, long. The next sessions tend to be shorter, perhaps half an hour or an hour in length. They may take place once a week, or

---

more or less frequently – this will be something for you and your therapist to discuss.

Therapists and counsellors charge different amounts. Some offer a reduced rate if you are on a low income but it is up to each professional to decide whether to do this. You and the therapist will agree how any times you should see them. Bear in mind that, as with many forms of help, good therapists will not suggest that you keep seeing them indefinitely. They will want to work with you so that you reach a point where their help is no longer needed, or perhaps needed only very occasionally.

Don't be afraid to tell the therapist if you need to limit the number of sessions because of the cost. If he or she knows you can afford only a small number of sessions, together you can work out how best to use that time.

You may well reach a point where you no longer feel the need to see the therapist. But if something happens to change that – perhaps another period of depressions arises – if you feel that going back to the therapist would help you, get in touch and ask about making another appointment. You should not feel that you have failed if you need help at some later stage – after all, you don't feel you've failed if you are physically ill more than once and need to see your GP each time!

Your GP may be able to suggest a therapist or counsellor you could approach. Or you can contact an organisation such as the British Association for Counselling and Psychotherapy (BACP; details on page 266), which can help you to find a trained therapist in your area.

In some areas, the NHS, charities and other not-for-profit organisations work together to provide different types of support for people with depression. Examples include local walking groups, taking part in the Green Gyms run by the British Trust for Conservation Volunteers (BTCV; contact details on page 267), or becoming a volunteer, or taking part in a local Time Bank UK initiative. Time Banks work by people helping each other in whatever way is possible and needed (contact details on page 283).

You can also find out about other volunteering opportunities from your local Age Concern.

Whether or not these types of support are available or suitable for you, your GP may refer you for:

- assessment by a consultant;
- out-patient clinic;
- day care;
- hospital stay;
- support from a community mental health nurse (formerly called community psychiatric nurse, CPN).

These types of support would most probably be provided through your local NHS psychiatric services (Box 14), although some social services departments and voluntary organisations offer day services for older people with depression and other mental health problems.

Age Concern Factsheet 6 *Finding help at home* may be helpful.

## Box 14. NHS psychiatric services

Psychiatry is a branch of medicine. It looks at disorders to do with people's behaviour and emotions, whether or not these are thought to be due to a particular disease of the brain. Within the service, you may find:

- Psychiatrists – doctors who diagnose and treat a wide range of mental health difficulties.
- Old age psychiatrists (also called psychogeriatricians) – doctors who have particular knowledge of older people's mental health problems.

You may also come across geriatricians, doctors who specialise in the physical illnesses and disabilities of older age; or neurologists, doctors who have expertise in disorders of the brain and the nervous system.

There are specialist hospitals that offer particular treatment and care for people with mental ill-health. These are usually called psychiatric hospitals.

## Depression and dementia

The relationship between dementia and depression is quite complex. The symptoms of dementia and depression – including withdrawal from social activities and general apathy – are very similar. As a result, someone who is severely depressed may be misdiagnosed as having dementia. On the other hand, a person with dementia may also become depressed.

Just as it is possible to have more than one physical illness or disability (eg to have diabetes and arthritis), so it is possible to have more than one mental health problem. In these situations it can be important to make sure that medication to treat one illness does not, because of any side effects, make worse any other mental health illnesses. Your GP or pharmacist should be able to advise about this.

*109*

# Dementia

The term 'dementia' describes more than 100 different brain disorders that result in a loss of brain function and which usually get worse over time. The most common types of dementia are:

- Alzheimer's disease;
- vascular dementia (resulting from brain damage caused by tiny strokes);
- Lewy body dementia (caused by abnormal collections of protein, called Lewy bodies, in the brain's nerve cells).

Typical symptoms include confusion, memory loss (especially short-term memory) and problems with speech and understanding. People may become agitated, or find it difficult to go about their usual daily business.

Having any of these symptoms does not necessarily mean you have dementia, however. For example, memory loss can also be a symptom of depression or stress. Similar symptoms can also arise as a result of problems with your thyroid, or because of vitamin deficiencies.

## Diagnosis

Getting a diagnosis is very important. You shouldn't be tempted to diagnose yourself, or assume that the confusion of someone you know must be because of dementia.

The first thing to do is see your GP and explain what has been happening. Ask them to tell you about the range of reasons that might be causing the problems. If your GP thinks that the possibility of dementia should be considered, they may refer you to a specialist consultant (perhaps an old age psychiatrist – a psychogeriatrician). The consultant will most likely see you at an appointment at a hospital out-patient clinic. Just because you are referred, however, does not mean you definitely have dementia.

There are various tests that may be carried out in order to diagnose your condition. They might include asking you some straightforward questions or getting you to do a simple task such as moving an object from one part of the room to another. A brain scan may be carried out, and blood samples taken.

Having a diagnosis of dementia can, like many diagnoses of ill-health, come as a huge shock. You may well want to talk to someone about this, and about what it means for you. The Alzheimer's Society (page 265) offers a telephone helpline for people (and their relatives/carers) with all types of dementia, not just Alzheimer's. They also have local groups, provide services, and offer information and advice.

## Treatment and support

There is no medication at present that can cure dementia, but there is some medication that can, temporarily at least, slow down the progression of the disease.

The National Institute for Health and Clinical Excellence (NICE) has told the NHS that three drugs – donepezil (Aricept), rivastigmine (Exelon) and galantamine (Reminyl) – should be available on NHS prescription for patients who could benefit from the treatment. These are only suitable for people with mild to moderate dementia, will only help temporarily and may not work for everyone.

Only a consultant can prescribe these drugs on the NHS. Your GP has to refer you to hospital for an assessment, which the consultant will carry out. If the consultant thinks the drugs would benefit you, they will write the first prescription. After this, your GP can write prescriptions for these drugs as usual, unless the consultant decides you should come back to hospital for regular check-ups and have your prescriptions drawn up then.

As with many other drugs, it is possible to obtain these through a private prescription. Bear in mind that, as well as the cost of the drugs, you may have to pay your GP for writing a private prescription as well as the pharmacist's fee for dispensing the medicine privately (see Chapter 10). But no one in the NHS should put you under pressure to buy these treatments privately. If you have difficulty obtaining these drugs through the NHS, contact your local Primary Care Trust or Patient Advice and Liaison Service. Your local Age Concern or the Alzheimer's Society may also be able to advise.

Some patients experience side effects from these treatments. As with all medication, you need to agree to take it after having considered the side effects, risks and benefits with your doctor. If any side effects cause you concern, see your GP as soon as you can; or talk to the pharmacist who issued the medicine.

The other types of drugs that are sometimes prescribed to older people with dementia are medicines called neuroleptics. These act as tranquillisers, and are sometimes used as a way of controlling behaviour such as 'wandering' among people living in care homes. But there are misgivings about using the drugs in this way, and many organisations suggest other approaches that can be used. The Alzheimer's Society has further information on this.

Aside from drug treatments, there are services to support you. Chapter 13 describes some of the different care options that you might want to consider for the longer term. However, with the right support, many people with dementia can remain living at home for a long time.

# Day hospitals and day care

Day care services can play an important part in supporting someone with dementia, as well as any family (unpaid, or informal) carers who may be involved. This type of support may also be available for older people with depression or other mental illnesses.

Day services may be provided in hospitals by the NHS or in centres run by social services departments or voluntary organisations. There are very few privately run day care services for older people with dementia.

Your GP can refer you to the day hospital. This may also form part of what the consultant recommends you receive from the NHS, after your assessment and diagnosis.

Day hospitals are typically open to patients between 10am and 4pm on weekdays, although some hospitals are expanding this service to offer longer hours, separate morning and afternoon sessions, and weekend openings.

What is actually offered at each day hospital varies but may include time in a small group undertaking an activity or taking part in reminiscence work (perhaps just with one member of staff). Many people attend for the whole day, in which case you will probably also be offered lunch.

Your going to the day hospital may help the consultant and nursing staff to gain a much more detailed picture of how dementia is affecting you, by spending time with you over a period of weeks. If you cannot get to the hospital yourself, the Patient Transport Service may provide door-to-door transport. This is often part of the local Ambulance Trust's service. Attending at the day hospital, and the transport to get you there, is free to you if it is all provided by the NHS.

By contrast, you may be asked to pay towards the costs of any day support arranged by social services or a voluntary organisation.

---

There is more about this in Age Concern Factsheet 6 *Finding help at home* and Factsheet 46 *Paying for care and support at home.*

---

Some support may be provided to you in your own home from community mental health nurses (Box 15), or perhaps from social services or a voluntary organisation. In some parts of the country, 'outreach' services have been developed, particularly for older people with dementia or depression (see page 109). This involves someone visiting you at home (perhaps once or twice a week) for a couple of hours, during which you and the worker share an activity. The type of activity will depend on your interests – for example, it could be

---

### Box 15. Community mental health nurses

Community mental health nurses (sometimes also called by their former name 'community psychiatric nurses' or CPNs) specialise in support for people with mental ill-health, and tend not to carry out any physical nursing. They may visit you at home as part of the overall assessment and to help check how you are; or they may visit to provide support for you in your everyday life.

They work with people of all ages and with all types of mental health difficulties. Your GP will be able to tell you whether you can contact the community mental health service direct and ask for their help or if you need to be referred by the GP or hospital consultant. Community mental health nurses are part of the NHS, so this support is provided free.

completing a jigsaw or crossword, painting, recording your life history, or looking at photographs. Outreach services such as these tend to be aimed at people who are so ill that they cannot attend a day hospital – for example, if the nature of their illness makes it extremely difficult for them to spend time with groups of people.

There are many other approaches to supporting older people with dementia. These include music therapy and gentle swimming exercises – both of which offer enjoyable and soothing experiences. There has also been a lot of work in recent years looking at how best to communicate with someone who has dementia. The research has uncovered several different ways this can be achieved, including 'non-verbal' forms of communication such as the way the person moves and other types of body language. The Dementia Services Development Centre at the University of Stirling (page 270) has researched this aspect.

## Schizophrenia

There are a number of more rare mental health problems that affect older people, including delirium, anxiety and late-onset schizophrenia.

Sometimes there is hostility and anxiety towards people who have been diagnosed with schizophrenia. This is often because of a belief that everyone with schizophrenia is violent. But this is not the case. Only a tiny number of people with schizophrenia ever commit a violent act. In the UK, the vast majority of violent crimes are committed by people who don't have this illness.

People often think that schizophrenia is to do with having a 'split personality'. But the illness is really to do with serious, or major, changes to what we believe and how we experience ordinary, everyday life. We all need to make sense of the world around us in order to function and get on with our lives. We're so used to doing this that we don't always realise just how much information our brain has to deal with to make sense of, for example, our getting on a bus and going shopping in a busy supermarket. During a schizophrenic episode, the person's experience and interpretation of the outside world are so affected that they can lose touch with reality. They may see or hear things that are not there and act in unusual ways in response to these hallucinations. These episodes can be very frightening for the person as well as for anyone witnessing this. They can last for weeks at a time.

Schizophrenia usually develops when someone is in their late teens or early 20s but can also start in an older person. Although the causes are unknown, episodes of schizophrenia seem to be connected with changes in some brain chemicals. It is thought that stressful experiences (and some recreational drugs, such as cannabis) may trigger an episode.

## Diagnosis

Doctors sometimes talk about the positive and negative symptoms of schizophrenia. Positive symptoms are abnormal experiences such as hallucinations, feeling that your thoughts are being taken over or delusions. Delusions are unusual beliefs, such as believing that someone is trying to kill you. These can be extremely frightening. It is important to remember that, for the person experiencing the delusions, these beliefs and feelings are real.

Although these positive symptoms are often the most dramatic, it is usually negative symptoms that cause the most problems. One reason for this is that negative symptoms last longer. They include tiredness, loss of concentration and lack of energy. People may have little or no motivation to do anything, and may struggle to manage household chores as a result.

# Treatment and support

Most people with schizophrenia are prescribed medication to reduce the positive symptoms. These may be prescribed for long periods of time, and can have unpleasant side effects.

However, not everyone needs drugs – or doesn't need to take them all the time. Some people find that, with other support (perhaps from a community mental health nurse) they are able to cope well with experiences such as hearing voices.

There are some differences in how older people with a psychotic illness (such as schizophrenia) access support services, compared with older people with other mental illnesses such as dementia and depression.

Like the word 'mental', 'psychotic' is sometimes used as an insult. But it is a proper medical term. To be psychotic means you have a psychosis – a severe mental illness. *The New Shorter Oxford Dictionary* defines a psychosis as:

'severe mental illness, derangements, or disorder involving a loss of contact with reality, frequently with hallucinations, delusions, or altered thought processes'

Sometimes, people in a severe phase of schizophrenia need to be admitted to hospital under the Mental Health Act 1983. This will be because of serious concerns about their current health. Anyone who is severely mentally ill might need hospital treatment, not just people with schizophrenia. People can become patients under the Mental Health Act either voluntarily (just as we agree to go into any hospital for treatment), or the Act can be used to require someone to be in hospital because of concerns about their safety or that of other people. This doesn't just apply to people with schizophrenia – it can apply to someone with depression, for example, or other mental health problems.

Some people with schizophrenia who want to make sure they have a say in what happens to them while in hospital carry 'crisis cards' or set up an *advance decision* (sometimes called an 'advance directive'), which make their wishes known (see page 126).

If you (or someone you know) experience the symptoms of schizophrenia, the first step will be to contact your GP, who can prescribe any medication needed. The GP can also refer you for other psychiatric help, including that provided by the local NHS Community Mental Health Team. In an emergency, if you are not sure what else to do, you can go to the Accident and Emergency department of your local hospital or dial 999 and ask for an ambulance to take you there. Or if you are already in contact with a community mental health nurse, you may have details of the team that can help in a mental health crisis, in which case you could contact them.

If you are diagnosed as having schizophrenia, you may want to contact the charity SANE (address on page 282).

Older people who are severely ill with a psychotic illness such as schizophrenia may need a package of treatment, care and support. Their care plans should be worked out according to the National Service Framework (NSF) for Mental Health – not the NSF for Older People. This involves what is known as the Care Programme Approach, which applies to everyone over the age of 16 who is under the care of a consultant psychiatrist. But this approach should be just as thorough for people over the age of 65 as the Single Assessment Process (SAP) used in all other cases where older people have health and care needs (see page 170).

# Mental health legislation

Most people have heard about 'being sectioned' under the Mental Health Act 1983. The term 'sectioning' refers to the differently numbered clauses (or sections) in the Act. These set out the various ways in which someone can be detained in hospital, as well as receive other services because of mental health needs.

Services provided under the Mental Health Act are free – regardless of whether they come from the NHS or via social services. This is particularly important in terms of what are sometimes called 'after-care services': support provided after a period of compulsory treatment (or 'detention') in hospital, and might, for example, involve moving permanently to live in a care home. In 2003 an important ruling about after-care services was published by the Local Government Ombudsman. This reminded local councils that no one should pay for after-care services until they are formally 'discharged' from this support – which happens when both the health and social services agree it can take place. There have also been some important court cases repeating what should happen after you are discharged in this way. If you have been receiving after-care services after compulsory hospital treatment for mental ill-health and are now being asked to pay towards future care services, you might want to check that the correct system is being applied. Contact Age Concern's Information Line (see page 264) for further details if this affects you.

## Being detained

Being detained can be a frightening experience that may come at a time when you are already very confused and agitated. But there are rules about this that must be followed.

You cannot be detained under the Mental Health Act until three people – two doctors and an approved social worker (ASW, a social worker specialising in mental health) – agree this is needed. The approved social worker then applies for the 'sectioning'.

One other person can apply for you to be 'sectioned' – your nearest relative. The Mental Health Act lists, in strict order, the people who may be considered as your nearest relative. The list starts with your spouse/person you live with as your partner, then goes on to adult children, and then parents. In your case, whoever is highest on the list is your 'nearest relative'.

Sectioning is usually done in one of two ways. The first is called a 'section 2 detention', because it comes under section 2 of the Mental Health Act 1983. This is when you have a mental disorder, and it has been decided that you need to be detained for assessment either for your own safety or for that of other people. You can be detained for up to 28 days and this cannot be extended, although you can be further detained under section 3 of the Act (see below). Your nearest relative must be told about this type of detention.

You can also be detained if you have a:

- mental illness
- mental impairment
- severe mental impairment
- psychopathic disorder

and you need to be detained for your own safety or that of other people, and treatment cannot be provided unless you are in hospital. This is sometimes called a 'section 3 detention'. You can be detained for up to six months before this must be reviewed; after that, it will be reviewed at least once a year. If you are going to be detained in this way, the approved social worker must tell your nearest relative before it happens. Your nearest relative can object, in which case the approved social worker has to come up with some other solutions that would meet your mental health needs.

You can start with assessment through a section 2 detention and then have a period of compulsory treatment through a section 3 detention.

You have the right to consult a solicitor, although your detention won't be delayed while you contact someone. But a solicitor would be able to give you legal advice about asking to be discharged from the section, for example. You will need a solicitor who knows about mental health law. This is not a free service, however; and you may be asked to pay something towards it, depending on your income. The exception is for appeals to the Mental Health Review Tribunal (see page 122), which is free. The charity MIND has information on solicitors specialising in mental health law, and about financial help with these costs (contact details on page 278).

You may also find it helpful to have an advocate. This is nothing to do with the law. An advocate is someone who will find out what you want and then speak for you, perhaps at meetings or other discussions. MIND may also offer advocacy support.

Under both types of section you can be prevented from leaving the hospital ward, but you can also be given permission to do so by the 'responsible medical officer' (RMO). Your consent to any treatment should be sought; however, some treatments can still be given to you even if you do not give consent:

- When you are incapacitated, which means you are unable to consent (see page 125).
- If you or someone else is in immediate danger; in this case, you can be given a limited amount of treatment to deal with this immediate danger.
- Medical treatment for mental disorder while you are detained.

The types of medical treatment you can be given without your consent include most treatments and care available on a psychiatric ward, such as nursing care and medication. It could include physical restraint. It can also include treatment that cannot be given without your co-operation, such as 'talking' treatments. It is not clear, however, that physical treatment, such as blood tests (associated with some psychiatric drugs), would be included. You might want to seek legal advice if this type of treatment is being proposed and you object to it. There are no time limits for this medical treatment.

There are also three exceptions to this arrangement:

- Psychiatric drugs can be given to you for three months. After that, an independent doctor, sent by the Mental Health Act Commission, must decide whether this treatment should continue. This doctor is called a 'second opinion appointed doctor' (SOAD) – but this has nothing to do with other types of second opinion.
- Electro-convulsive therapy (ECT) cannot be used without your consent unless a second opinion appointed doctor has decided this treatment should be given to you (although in an emergency, ECT can be given before the second opinion appointed doctor arrives).
- Psychosurgery, such as a lobotomy, cannot be given without your informed consent and a second opinion that this surgery is in your best interests.

While compulsorily in hospital, you have some other rights:

- The right to apply to the Mental Health Review Tribunal, asking them to review the decision about your being discharged. This right is often used by people who feel much better following treatment and who disagree with the view of their doctors that they should remain in hospital.
- The right to complain about any aspect of your care to the Mental Health Act Commission (MHAC). This is a Special Health Authority and is independent of the hospital. The Commission will probably expect you to use the hospital complaints procedure in the first instance (see Chapter 16).

You can also still handle your own money and make other decisions while in hospital (such as voting in local or general elections), unless there is a question about your mental capacity to do so (see page 125).

There is another way of being detained. This applies to people who are mentally ill and have been charged with, or found guilty of, a criminal offence. This is not dealt with in this book.

*It is important to remember that many people also receive treatment in psychiatric hospitals and units as voluntary patients. This means they are free to discharge themselves at any stage, just as they would be if they were in hospital because of physical ill-health. It also means that no treatment can be given without their consent – just as would be the case for treatment for physical conditions.*

In the summer of 2004, the Government published a draft Mental Health Bill. This aims to replace the current legislation (although it must first pass through the usual Parliamentary processes). Among other changes, the draft Bill seeks to change the law regarding compulsory treatment. Instead of only being able to require someone to receive treatment in hospital, it sets out proposals whereby doctors could require patients to comply with treatment being received in their own homes. This would include being required to take medication as directed, or to receive other treatment. It is not yet clear whether, or when, this Bill might become the law.

## Consent and decision-making

There are many references to consent throughout this book. We need to give our consent before almost all NHS services (and other health treatments) can go ahead – except for compulsory detention in hospital and emergency treatment in some situations (see page 157).

We are free to go ahead and agree to treatment, or to refuse this – even when we know that what we are refusing may hasten our death.

This treatment could be an operation, or taking medicine, or having physiotherapy or any other of the NHS's services. As long as we can express our views and make our own decisions, the wishes of other people – whether they are doctors, relatives, religious leaders, campaigning groups or anyone else – cannot be imposed on us.

But problems arise when we are not able to either give or refuse to give our consent, or when we cannot express our views.

## The Bournewood case

In the autumn of 2004, the European Court of Human Rights gave a final ruling on a case that had already gone through the UK's courts, taking some years to do so.

What has become known as 'the Bournewood case' involved a man who was not able to express his wishes regarding his current treatment and longer term care because of autism. A doctor, who had been called out when he became agitated at a day centre he attended, admitted him to hospital. His two paid carers, with whom he lived, went to court on his behalf when the hospital was still refusing to discharge him two months later.

He had not been detained under the Mental Health Act 1983. But doctors ruled that, as he was 'compliant' with being in hospital, he did not need to be formally detained. His carers argued that, because he was not able to express his views, his compliance at being in hospital should not be viewed as agreeing to be there.

The European Court ruled that his human rights had been breached because he had been deprived of his liberty. Doctors and other health professionals had taken full control over his liberty and treatment. Had the man been detained (sectioned) under the Mental Health Act, he (or someone acting for him) would have had the right to a review of his continuing hospital stay. But because he was 'voluntarily' in hospital, it was only the professionals who had already decided he should remain there who would review his care.

This case is very important for anyone – including any older person – who is not able to consent to or refuse or to express their views about treatment because of a lack of 'mental capacity'.

## Mental capacity

'Mental capacity' means having the ability to make your own decisions. Most of us can make most decisions for ourselves, although we often seek advice and information from others to help us do so – whether from solicitors or financial advisers, doctors, friends, charities or other sources.

We may all be uncertain from time to time about whether we are making the right decision. Being able to make your own decisions means you may get some decisions wrong. You may look back and wish you had done something differently. But at the time you were able to understand what you were deciding about. This included understanding, as well as you could at the time, the implications of making that decision as well as the implications of not making it. You were able to understand the issues, gather information and seek advice, and you were able to express your decisions, whether in writing or verbally or by some other means.

Some people are able to make some, but not all, decisions. For example, someone might be able to decide what to have for lunch and where to sit while eating it – but be unable to decide whether the person they sit next to is to be trusted to look after their gold watch. This isn't because they are uncertain about these things but because:

- they cannot understand all the aspects of this situation; *or*
- they cannot comprehend the implications of their decision (one way or another); *or*

- whilst they may be able to show you through body language, facial expressions or other means, what clothes they have decided to wear, they cannot express more complicated matters – even with help and support.

Mostly the inability to communicate a particular decision is as a result of disability, illness or accident. Occasionally it is one of the side effects of prescribed medicine. Sometimes people can make all their own decisions at some times but not all the time – for example, if they have an illness or disability that fluctuates and so affects their decision-making abilities.

Most older people have been making their own decisions throughout their lives. It is the onset of an illness, disability or accident (such as a head injury) that tends to affect their ability to continue to make all these decisions.

Sometimes, if people know they have a condition such as dementia that means their ability to make their own decisions may reduce over time as the disease progresses, they decide to write down now what they want to happen in certain circumstances. They do so using either an advance decision or an advance statement.

## Advance decisions

Advance decisions (sometimes also called 'Living Wills' or advance directives) are different from advance statements (see page 129). Advance decisions offer you an opportunity to refuse particular medical treatments in advance.

If you decide to refuse treatment that is offered, the doctors must abide by your decision – even if they wish you had made a different decision. However, if you are no longer able to decide, doctors can look at your advance decision to see what types of treatment you have said earlier you would refuse, and the circumstances in which you would refuse them.

At the moment, although there is no Act of Parliament relating to advance decisions that applies to England, Wales or Northern Ireland, your advance decision would be taken as binding provided that:

- when you wrote it you had the mental capacity to understand (and had been informed about) all the consequences of refusing treatment;
- you intended the refusal to apply in the situation that has now arisen;
- you were not under pressure from other people in reaching your decision.

Although some people set out to describe the sort of situation in which they would not wish to have treatment that is aimed only at sustaining life, this is unlikely to be legally binding. But doctors would take it into account in such a situation because, if nothing else, it tells them about your personal views on the subject.

Advance decisions are not popular with everyone. But you do not have to make one, nor should you do so if you have any doubts about them. If you do make an advance decision, most advice suggests that you review it every few years and update it as needed. Put it in writing and make sure that other people know it exists and how to get hold of it. You may decide to always carry a copy with you, in your bag or wallet. You may also want to tell your GP, or a hospital consultant if you are under their care, about the advance decision you have made.

Even if you have made an advance decision, it only comes into effect if there is a time when you cannot make that sort of decision. If you still have the mental capacity to decide, you will be asked to do so as usual.

Although some people think that making an advance decision is only to do with refusing care at the end of your life, your advance decision can cover *any* medical treatment. You might want to make sure that everyone knows you would always refuse to have all your teeth taken out, for example; or that you would never accept eye surgery under local anaesthetic (although you might agree to this being carried out under a general anaesthetic) because you have a fear of people touching your eyes.

But you should also note that you cannot use an advance decision to:

- Refuse the basic nursing care that is essential if you are to be comfortable, such as personal washing and mouth care.
- Refuse the offer of food or drink by mouth in order to starve yourself.
- Refuse anything designed to keep you as comfortable as possible, such as pain-killers.

Some of the debate in Parliament during 2004 and 2005 about the Mental Capacity Bill has been about whether 'basic care' should also include artificial methods of nutrition and hydration (food and drink).

The Alzheimer's Society and MIND have further information about advance decisions, including how to record these. You may also find Age Concern Information Sheet 5 *Living Wills* helpful.

The law in England, Wales and Northern Ireland means that, if you lack the mental capacity to decide about your medical treatment, ultimately the medical team will decide on your behalf. They should ask your relatives and close friends about your views, and what they think you might have wanted to do (this is not the same as asking your relatives what *they* want) – but the ultimate decision does not lie with your relatives, nor even your spouse or partner. The medical team will take what they are told about you into consideration when reaching a decision. This decision has to be in your best interests – not the interests of the NHS, of individual staff, or of your relatives or anyone else – only in your interests.

If your relatives, or someone else close to you, disagree with the doctors' decision (because, for example, they think you would have made a different decision or because they don't think the decision is in your best interests), they can ask the High Court to rule on the matter. The courts generally hear such cases very quickly, sometimes within a matter of days if not hours. At present, although there are various ways in which you can manage the finances of someone else, you cannot make health and welfare decisions on their behalf.

The situation is different in Scotland, where the Adults with Incapacity (Scotland) Act 2000 enables you to nominate (in advance, while you have the mental capacity to do this) a 'welfare attorney' who will have the power to refuse or consent to your medical treatment if you cannot do this at the time. The attorney might be your spouse or partner, or another relative or friend or someone else you choose who agrees to take on this role. The word 'attorney' has nothing to do with the legal profession.

There is currently a proposal for something similar in England and Wales – a welfare Lasting Power of Attorney. This is in the Mental Capacity Bill, which has been going through Parliament during 2004/2005. It is not yet clear whether, and when, this might become the law – but if it is passed and becomes an Act of Parliament, the earliest date it would come into effect would be sometime in 2006.

## Advance statements

Unlike an advance decision, which allows you to record your refusal of medical treatment in advance, an advance statement is a way for you to record your wishes and views. This is about you saying what you *would* like to happen, and what is important to you in all aspects of life – not just medical care. For example, you might use an advance statement to record your favourite things to eat, television programmes to watch, and hobbies and interests.

In the summer of 2004, a case was brought against the General Medical Council (GMC) concerning their guidelines on end-of-life treatment, which are followed by doctors in the UK. The case was brought by Mr Burke (who has a neurological condition that will get progressively worse). He has made an advance statement that he wants everything possible done to prolong his life, if at the time he is no longer able to express that view.

The High Court ruled that doctors should follow what has been written in an advance statement, wherever possible; the case was being appealed by the General Medical Council, however, so was not yet firmly settled by early 2005. If you have queries about this, contact Age Concern's Information Line – see page 264.

None of us has an absolute right in law to insist that all and every medical treatment is provided to us by the NHS. This doesn't change when we are at the end of our lives. Some people do not want to have life-prolonging treatment and, when they have the capacity to make that decision and say so, this has to be respected. One example of this was the case of Miss B (see page 8). She had the mental capacity to refuse to continue the artificial support she was receiving, knowing that this would hasten her death. In contrast, other people who have the capacity to decide, or communicate their decisions, might decide that they do want everything possible done.

If you have particular views about the end-of-life treatment you would want for yourself but are worried that your wishes won't be followed (or known about), you may want to think about recording this view in an advance statement. As with advance decisions, you should make sure people close to you and/or involved in your care know it exists and, preferably, have some idea at least of what it says.

There are other ways advance statements can be used. For example, you can use them to record details about your life such as what you have done and what has been important to you. Or you might want to nominate someone to be consulted when decisions have to be made (such as deciding about medical treatment) – but you should make sure the person agrees to this.

You cannot use an advance statement to:

- Demand care that the health professionals involved in your care consider inappropriate for you.
- Ask for anything that is against the law – such as euthanasia or help to commit suicide.

# Other issues

If you have been diagnosed with a mental illness, you may be eligible for disability benefits; you may also be entitled to reductions in the amount you have to pay in Council Tax – see Age Concern Factsheets, listed below for more information. You may want to contact any of the organisations in this chapter for further advice and information about the effect of your diagnosis on different aspects of your life. For example, if you are diagnosed with dementia, you are obliged to tell the Driver and Vehicle Licensing Agency (DVLA); but you may also be eligible for the Blue Badge parking scheme for people with disabilities.

The following Age Concern Factsheets may be helpful:

34 *Attendance Allowance and Disability Living Allowance*
21 *The Council Tax and older people*
6 *Finding help at home*

# Chapter 9

# Chiropody and foot care

This chapter looks at how to get NHS chiropody services, and what to do if services are not provided. It also explains about private chiropody (including finding a chiropodist and paying privately), and toenail-cutting services. It explains different terms that you might come across, and looks at some of the links between foot care and certain diseases and illnesses.

## Chiropodists and podiatrists

The first thing you may notice, when looking for a professional to help look after the health of your feet, is that two terms are used – 'chiropodist' and 'podiatrist'. Some people say that 'podiatry' is simply the American term for 'chiropody'. Others say that podiatry is a particular type of chiropody, where the professional focuses on the bones in someone's feet and what might be called the 'mechanics' of walking – how we actually walk (sometimes also called 'biomechanics'). This chapter uses the terms 'chiropody' and 'chiropodist'.

Chiropodists diagnose and treat abnormalities and diseases of the lower limb. They can also advise on preventing foot problems and on proper foot care and footwear; and can perform minor surgical procedures such as nail surgery.

In the UK, people must have registered with the Health Professions Council by 8 July 2005 if they want to call themselves 'chiropodists'. This registration means that people have reached a certain standard in their professional training. After 8 July 2005, it will be against the law to call yourself a chiropodist (or podiatrist) if you are not registered in this way. This applies whether people are working in the NHS, in a charity or in the private sector (perhaps running their own business).

People who work in beauty salons offering nail-cutting services and pedicures will not be able to call themselves chiropodists unless they are registered as such with the Health Professions Council. They can call themselves 'foot care professionals' or 'pedicurists' instead.

This arrangement replaces the previous system of state registration. Some professionals may continue to use 'SRCh' or 'State registered chiropodist' after their name, but you should now be looking for someone who says they are registered with the Health Professions Council, or holds one of the following qualifications:

- MChS (Member of the Society of Chiropodists and Podiatrists)
- FChS (Fellow of the Society of Chiropodists and Podiatrists)
- FPod(S) (Fellow of the College of Podiatrists or the Society of Chiropodists & Podiatrists).

If you think the chiropodist has behaved badly or the standard of care has not been good, you can contact the Health Professions Council. This applies both to private chiropodists and those who work in the NHS. If you are concerned about the NHS treatment you have received, you can also use the NHS complaints procedure – see Chapter 16.

## Other terms

There are two other terms that you may come across, depending on the type of help you need with your feet:

- orthotics
- prosthetics.

An *orthosis* is something that either corrects how you walk or helps you to walk or place your feet more easily. This could include a built-up shoe (if one leg is longer than the other), or a brace that supports your leg or foot if it is twisted in some way. Someone who works with orthoses is likely to be called an orthotics technician – and 'orthotics' may be the name of the department or organisation where they work.

*Prosthesis* is the name for something that replaces a missing part of your body – for example, an artificial replacement leg or hand. In foot care, a prosthetic technician may work with chiropodists and orthotic technicians if, for example, someone has one artificial foot and needs appropriate footwear for this and their other foot.

In hospitals, the department that concentrates on matters to do with your bones and joints is likely to be called 'orthopaedics'. If you need help with your legs and feet, your GP or an NHS chiropodist will refer you.

---

If you have problems finding shoes, slippers or other footwear because your feet are different sizes, or are swollen or particularly sensitive or there are other difficulties, the Disabled Living Foundation has information sheets that may help you (contact details on page 272).

---

# Why is foot care important?

Chiropodists will tell you that your feet are one of the most vulnerable parts of your body. They are certainly likely to be one of the most used areas of the body. Foot care is important for three main reasons:

- The condition of our feet can alert professionals to other health problems, such as diabetes or poor circulation which, if untreated and severe, can result eventually in part of the foot or even leg having to be amputated.

■ We are likely to walk more if our feet are healthy and strong.

■ Healthy feet are important in keeping our balance and, thus, avoid falling over.

# Finding a chiropodist

There are many reasons why people need to find a chiropodist. You may have particular health problems with your feet, perhaps because of another medical condition such as diabetes. Or other disabilities may make it difficult for you to bend to get close enough to care for your feet; or you may have difficulty using nail scissors because of arthritis in your hands. Or you may want to have your feet checked, and get some advice on how best to look after them or what footwear to buy.

People who like to have pedicures and other, more beauty-based, treatments are more likely to want to find a pedicurist rather than a chiropodist. Pedicurists may come to your home or offer treatments in beauty salons. You have to pay for these sorts of treatments. You can find a pedicurist in the local telephone directory, under the heading 'Beauty treatments' or 'Beauty salons'. They are likely to have been trained in different types of beauty therapy, including giving pedicures – but you can always ask about their training when you make the appointment.

# Chiropody from the NHS

Over the last 20 years the amount and type of chiropody services provided by the NHS have changed quite significantly. As explained in Chapter 1, this is an example of there being no absolute right for every person in England to receive chiropody care. It is also an example of the differences around the country as to how much help is available from the NHS and who receives this. Each area sets its own 'rules' or criteria, and these can vary. In order to receive NHS chiropody, your reason for needing it must 'fit' the local criteria. If the NHS provides this, you will not have to pay for it.

You should be able to find out about NHS chiropody services and eligibility criteria from your GP or your local Primary Care Trust.

The obvious starting point for your getting NHS chiropody will be that you are experiencing some kind of problem with your feet or you have a health condition that could affect your feet – and, in turn, your overall health. An example of this is Type 2 diabetes.

## Diabetes and other medical problems

Type 2 diabetes is where the body cannot produce enough insulin – or the right kind. This sort of diabetes may not develop until after you have reached the age of 40.

If it is severe enough, diabetes can lead to poor circulation, resulting in foot ulcers and sores. In extreme circumstances, someone with diabetes may face losing part of their foot or even leg. This is why foot care is particularly important for people with diabetes. In 2004, the National Institute for Health and Clinical Excellence (NICE) issued guidelines to the NHS on foot care for people with Type 2 diabetes. This stressed:

- That people with diabetes should have their feet and lower legs examined regularly (this might form part of their annual medical check-up).
- This examination should: check for changes in skin colour, for ulcers and sores, the flow of blood in the foot, and footwear (to

make sure this is not creating pressure); assess the person's level of risk for developing foot problems in the future; agree a 'care plan' of what needs to be done.

The guidelines also say that if any NHS professional reports a change in the condition of your feet – such as a change of colour (to black, red, blue or white), or new swelling, ulcers or broken skin – you should be seen by the appropriate health team within 24 hours.

If you have diabetes and have any concerns about the condition of your feet, you could:

- make an appointment to see your GP or the nurse (who may run a clinic for people with diabetes) at the GP surgery;
- contact your district nurse, if someone already visits you;
- contact the NHS chiropody service where you live (it may be called 'podiatry' or 'foot care' in your area);
- contact NHS Direct or your local Patient Advice and Liaison Service and ask them whom you should speak to or see locally, if you cannot easily do any of the first three, above.

Or you might want to contact the charity Diabetes UK, which runs Careline, a telephone advice service (address on page 271).

If you have feet problems because of other medical issues (such as problems with circulation as a result of heart disease), ask your GP or the surgery's nurse for advice. The GP should be able to tell you about local NHS chiropody services, and to refer you, if needed.

If you have recently had a fall and have been referred to your local NHS Falls Prevention Service, you may find that it runs clinics that include input from a chiropodist (see Chapter 7). Or there may be a Healthy Living Centre in your area that offers foot clinics or sessions with an NHS chiropodist.

Depending on where you live, chiropody may be available from different parts of the NHS – perhaps your local community NHS Trust or one of the examples mentioned above. If you cannot easily find out about your local NHS chiropody service, do keep trying: ask at your GP surgery or NHS Direct for help with this. Every part of the country provides some chiropody – the question you need answering is how much and where from in your area.

# Nail cutting

The number of nail-cutting services provided by the NHS has been reducing for some time. These may be needed by people who can't reach their toenails, or can't see to cut them, or can't hold nail scissors.

Some areas do still have an NHS nail-cutting service but you may find that this is not offered very often. For example, an NHS chiropodist may be available to cut your toenails but only every three months. Most people's nails need to be cut more often – perhaps every six weeks.

Many parts of the country, however, do not offer nail cutting through the NHS unless you have a health condition that puts you 'at risk' of foot-related problems. Instead, there may be a simple nail-cutting service available through a local voluntary organisation. Contact your local Age Concern to see if such a service is offered in your area. Unless it is funded by the NHS, though, you may be asked to pay towards this.

If you feel you need a nail-cutting service from the NHS but you are told it is not available from the NHS in your area, or you feel that what is on offer from the NHS isn't enough, you can:

■ Complain to your local Primary Care Trust, which is responsible for providing and arranging NHS services in your areas via the Patient Advice and Liaison Service. (Chapter 16 tells you about complaining.)

- Ask your GP if they will make the case for nail-cutting services locally – or consider providing this in their surgery.
- Contact a campaigning charity, such as Age Concern England.
- Write to your MP and ask him or her to raise this with the Secretary of State for Health.

Most of these suggestions are to do with campaigning to achieve change in the future. There is more about this in Chapter 18. Although campaigning is important, you may still need help with cutting your toenails now. If you are using other local health and social care services, such as a local Falls Prevention Service (if you have recently had a fall), or a day centre, or are living in a care home, you may find that a nail-cutting service is provided as part of this support. Whether this is provided by the NHS, and so is free to you, is another matter. If it is not, but there is a local nail-cutting service provided by a voluntary organisation, that organisation will tell you how much you might be asked to pay towards the service.

Whatever NHS chiropody exists in your area should be available to you no matter where you live –in your own home, or in a sheltered flat, or in a care or nursing home. And, like all NHS services, it should not matter if you could afford to pay privately for chiropody. NHS chiropody has to be based on your need for this service matching up with the local criteria. In the end, although you may also want to complain and campaign, if you cannot get NHS chiropody, you may have to look outside the NHS for chiropody. (See also Chapter 13.)

# Private chiropodists

Chiropodists have to be registered whether they work in the NHS or privately. Many will have attended the same training courses. Some private chiropodists may even have previously worked in the NHS. The big difference is that private chiropodists run their own businesses – and they charge the people who use their services.

When you arrange to see a private chiropodist, you will have to pay them yourself. How much you pay will vary, depending on:

- whether they come to where you live or you visit their clinic;
- the type of treatment you need.

If you arrange to see a private chiropodist, make sure you know how much you will have to pay before you go. Knowing this should mean there are no nasty shocks at the end of the session – and no embarrassment for you or the chiropodist.

At your first appointment, the chiropodist should give you some idea of whether you should see them again, and how often. Some people can feel that, because the chiropodists charge for these visits, they will be trying to get you to visit as often as possible because then they will earn more. But this should not be the case – especially if the chiropodist is a skilled professional. Their training means they expect to see you as little as possible. This is because part of their job is to help you get better or to manage the problem more effectively.

If you have concerns about the chiropodist you are seeing, or the advice you are being given, try to see a different chiropodist in your area. But remember that you will still have to pay for the advice and treatment you have received, plus the advice of the second chiropodist.

---

Organisations you might like to contact, if you have questions about the registration or training of chiropodists, are: the Health Professions Council, the Society of Chiropodists and Podiatrists, the British Chiropody Podiatry Association, the Associated Chiropodists and Podiatrists Union, the Institute of Chiropodists and Podiatrists, and the Alliance of Private Sector Chiropody and Podiatry Practitioners. These organisations are listed in the Appendix.

---

# Chapter 10

# Pharmacy

This chapter looks at your rights to receive medicines on prescription. It describes the role of pharmacies (or chemist shops) and pharmacists, and also looks at who can prescribe and what is available on prescription from the NHS.

## NHS prescriptions

Everyone aged 60 or over who is entitled to receive NHS prescriptions receives the items listed free of charge. The amount that younger adults pay in England for their NHS prescriptions is set by government; some of this group may qualify for help with these charges if they are on a low income. Some younger adults receive free prescriptions – for example, those who have certain conditions such as diabetes and those who cannot get out of their home alone.

If you are 60 or older, you do not have to pay for any drugs or other treatments that you receive on the NHS. But you do have to pay for:

- items on private prescriptions;
- 'over-the-counter' treatments (see Box 16).

---

**Box 16. Over-the-counter treatments**

The NHS may not prescribe some items for you. These may be types of medication you can buy 'over the counter' (without a prescription) from pharmacists (sometimes known as 'the chemist'). Typical 'over-the-counter' drugs and treatments include ordinary pain-killers (eg aspirin or paracetamol) – although your GP may prescribe these for you, in which case there will be no charge if you are aged 60 or older – cough syrup and throat sweets.

---

The types of drugs (medication) available on prescription from the NHS change over time. For example, some of the treatments to help you stop smoking (such as some nicotine replacement patches) are now available on the NHS. The Pharmacy Pricing Authority and the Secretary of State for Health regularly update this 'NHS list', and give this information to everyone who prescribes NHS medicines (after October 2005, the Pharmacy Pricing Authority will be called the Prescription Pricing Authority). This includes the drugs and treatments that the National Institute for Health and Clinical Excellence (NICE) has said should be provided by the NHS. The broad rule of thumb about the 'NHS list' is that the NHS prescribes what it accepts has a medical benefit. This is usually medicine – pills, ointments, injections – but it can include other treatments such as oxygen supplies for people with severe breathing problems.

All drugs have to be paid for, one way or another. So even if you don't pay for the items on your NHS prescription, the NHS still has to buy the drugs and other treatments from the companies that make them. In each area, this 'drugs bill' is the responsibility of your local Primary Care Trust.

Primary Care Trusts and GPs work together to make sure that patients receive what they need within the budget available for the cost of drugs. This means that the doctor may prescribe what are called 'generic' medicines. Generic medicines are those marketed without a brand name. An example of brand and generic medicines that might be familiar to you are the pain-killers Nurofen and ibuprofen. Nurofen is the brand name; ibuprofen is the generic name. They have different names but are very similar drugs. You might be prescribed a generic drug rather than a particular brand whose name you know. One reason for this may be that the generic medicine is cheaper than the brand name drug. But you should still receive the drug that is right for your condition, so, if you have queries, ask the person who is prescribing it for you (see below). You could also ask the pharmacist (chemist) who will give you the drugs when you hand in your prescription (see page 148).

Sometimes doctors may decide to 'prescribe' a course of treatment that isn't about taking a drug. They may believe that a different approach would help improve a patient's health, such as:

- joining a walking group;
- going to a Stop Smoking Clinic.

This type of support may be available to you free of charge from the NHS in your area, but your doctor has to recommend you (refer you) in order for you to be able to take part. It is this recommendation that doctors mean when they talk about this kind of 'prescribing'.

# Taking medication

As with all other treatments, for the vast majority of people it is up to you whether to take the drugs you have been prescribed. There are occasional exceptions, and these are described in Chapter 8. But you need to be clear that there are likely to be consequences for you if you do not take your medicines. You need to be given information about this (see Chapter 17). The most likely outcome of your not taking prescribed medication will be that you do not get better, or at least not very quickly. But you can still choose to refuse to take the medication, even so.

If you do decide to take your medicines, it is important that you:

- take only medication that has been prescribed for you;
- take only the dosage prescribed for you (how often, and how much each time).

It's particularly important that you don't take medication meant for other people. Even if someone else has the same illness or disability as you, there are lots of factors that are taken into account when prescribing medicine. This means that what you need may be very different from what someone else receives.

There are devices available to help people who find it difficult to remember to take their tablets. These are usually on sale at local chemists' shops. One design is a small box divided into seven sections, one for each day of the week. If you put out the pills you need to take at the start of each week in the correct sections, you will be able to see at a glance whether or not you have taken that day's dosage. Other designs allow you to put out pills for different times on each day of the week. Some people find a simple approach, such as setting an alarm clock to go off at the time a pill must be taken, and putting this next to the pills that must be taken, can also be helpful. There are also pill boxes that have an alarm built in. But if you (or someone you know) are struggling with this, talk to your GP or your local pharmacist to see if they have other ideas. The Disabled Living Foundation also has advice and information about taking medicines (contact details on page 272).

If it is difficult for you to collect your prescribed medication (perhaps because your illness or disability means you are unable to leave your home), ask your GP and pharmacist about help in getting your medicine. If there are other difficulties, such as sight problems that mean you need a large-print label stating how often to take your medication, ask the pharmacist for help with this.

If other professionals are involved in caring for you, such as home care workers who come to you at your home or staff in the care home where you live, they should keep a record of the medicine you have taken each day.

# Private prescriptions

If you see your GP as a private patient, you will probably be given private prescriptions. This means that you pay the chemist for the cost of the drugs prescribed. The chemist will also ask you to pay them a small dispensing fee for their services – this amount varies. You can ask your doctor how much the drugs you are being prescribed will cost.

# Who can prescribe?

It may surprise you to know that there are four groups of professionals who can prescribe:

- doctors
- dentists
- nurses
- pharmacists.

There are limits to the types of drugs that can be prescribed by dentists, nurses and pharmacists. Only nurses and pharmacists who have had extra training to prescribe are allowed to do so.

There are proposals to allow other health professionals, such as physiotherapists, radiographers, chiropodists and optometrists, also to prescribe. But this change is not yet certain to happen.

It might well be that the health care professional you are seeing knows you need a certain drug or treatment but they cannot prescribe this for you unless they have undergone the necessary training. Instead, they have to refer you to your GP (or to the consultant if you are in hospital).

# Repeat prescriptions

When you are coming to the end of the drugs you have been taking, you may need another supply. You can get this by asking for a 'repeat prescription' from the health professional who prescribed the medicine you are just finishing. Usually this just means that you go to the surgery (or clinic) and collect another prescription for the same drugs without needing to see anyone. But if your health has changed at all since you last saw someone, or you think there were any side effects from the medicine you have been taking, you should make an appointment to talk to someone about this – probably your GP.

Some GP practices have introduced new systems for repeat prescriptions, whereby you ring a separate telephone number and leave a message. Others are beginning to use the computer-based (electronic) patient-record system to transfer repeat prescription details direct to a particular pharmacy. There are plans for this arrangement to become more common but it will probably be quite some time before it happens in every area.

If you are older and need a repeat prescription, you may in any case be asked to come into the surgery or clinic. The National Service Framework for Older People recommends that NHS patients over the age of 75 should have their medication reviewed at least once a year. Those over the age of 75 who take four or more medicines should have a review every six months. One of the reasons for this is that people in this age group who take four or more different types of drugs are more likely than anyone else to have a fall. Another reason is that, if you need to take this amount of medicine, you may benefit from some regular checks on your health.

There are proposals to transfer the main responsibility for repeat dispensing from GPs to community pharmacists at some point in the future. This is because a repeat prescription is essentially about getting more of the same medicine. If it is implemented, you will be able to get your regular prescriptions direct from a community pharmacist. The person who prescribes the medicine (probably a GP but see also page 142) will say how long this arrangement should continue before he or she would want to review the medication. But this system is not yet in place.

Doctors who see patients on a private basis will have their own system for repeat prescriptions. It is up to them whether or not to provide a repeat prescription. They may ask you to pay a small fee for this, and will probably want you to put your request in writing.

## When you are away from the UK

If you are going to be out of the UK on holiday or on business, there are some restrictions about medicines that you may need to know about.

Firstly, there are some drugs that you are not allowed to take out of the UK, whether or not you are being prescribed these on the NHS. Your GP or pharmacist will be able to advise about this, or you can contact the Drugs Branch of the Home Office (see page 277) and ask about it.

Secondly, your GP can only write you an NHS prescription for a maximum of three months' supply. If you are going to be out of the UK for longer, your GP can write you a private prescription. As well as paying for the cost of the medicine and the chemist's fee, you will probably have to pay your GP for writing the prescription.

Thirdly, you can ask your GP to prescribe drugs to take abroad 'just in case' – for example, antibiotics in case of a stomach bug. But this type of prescription is not available on the NHS. Again, your GP can write you a private prescription for this type of medicine, which you will have to pay for.

Chapter 13 has more information about health care while you are away from the UK or move to live abroad permanently.

## Pharmacists

Pharmacists specialise in the actual medicines that we take. They are trained professionals, and must be registered with the Royal Pharmaceutical Society of Great Britain in order to practise. We talk about pharmacists dispensing medicine. This is because part of their work is to make sure that the right medicine is given (or 'dispensed') to you.

Pharmacists work in many different settings. They may be employed direct by the NHS and work in a hospital, for example. Or they may run their own pharmacy business and provide some pharmacy services to the NHS under a contract. Or they may work for large chains of shops such as Boots The Chemist or Lloyds Chemists.

One of their most important roles is to make sure that medicines (whether on prescription or bought over the counter) are supplied safely and correctly. They can also advise on the different aspects of taking medicines, such as side effects and dosage. Pharmacists can also help with:

- Disposing of medicines that are no longer needed or are 'out of date'.
- Repeat dispensing.
- Suggesting other health care professionals you should talk to.
- Giving advice for minor problems such as:
  - allergies (including hay fever);
  - aches and pains (including toothache and mild rheumatic pain);
  - infections and viruses (such as coughs and cold sores).
- Recommending over-the-counter medicines.

## Out-of-hours pharmacies

It is up to your local Primary Care Trust what arrangements it makes for out-of-hours pharmacy services. 'Out-of-hours services' means local chemists that are open to dispense medicines when other pharmacies are shut – typically in the evenings, weekends and Bank Holidays.

In many areas this involves a 'duty rota', where pharmacies take it in turns to be on duty at night or at the weekend. Most local newspapers print details of out-of-hours pharmacy arrangements, or you can find out what is available in your area either by ringing NHS Direct (see page 25) or by searching on the website www.nhsdirect.nhs.uk.

## Chapter 11

# Going to hospital

This chapter looks at going into hospital for treatment, whether as an in-patient (where you stay at least overnight) or as an out-patient at a clinic or for day surgery. It also describes going overseas for NHS-funded treatments, discusses the situation for private patients and looks at different aspects of being in hospital.

There are three ways of being a hospital patient:

- **As an out-patient** If you are referred for diagnosis by, or a second opinion from, a hospital consultant, or for tests to help with this diagnosis, you are an out-patient. You won't stay overnight. Your visit may take only a few minutes or, if you having lots of tests and investigations carried out (such as X-rays or brain scans), you may be there all day. You may also be referred to an out-patient clinic or other service. This could include hospital day services for older people with dementia (see Chapter 8), or physiotherapy sessions (Chapter 7), Falls Clinics (Chapter 7) or 'stop smoking' clinics (Chapter 3). See also page 166.
- **As an in-patient** This is where you need to stay in hospital at least overnight. Much of this chapter looks at being an in-patient in hospital.
- **As a day patient** This is where surgery is carried out in the daytime, and you don't need to stay overnight. See page 165.

# Being admitted to hospital

If you are going to be staying in an NHS hospital, there are two ways you can be admitted:

■ the unplanned way, via an Accident and Emergency (A&E) hospital department;

■ for surgery that has been planned for you – this is usually called elective surgery, and is not emergency treatment.

There are national targets for both A&E and planned (or elective surgery) admissions to hospital that the NHS must meet. One of these targets is that you should be seen at an A&E department within four hours of your arriving. Once you have been seen, and depending on why you have come to A&E, staff will tell you which of the following will happen next:

■ the problem is minor and you can go back home because nothing needs to be done; *or*

■ the problem is best dealt with by your GP or another NHS primary care service; *or*

■ that you will be treated there and then and, because this treatment will be enough, you will then be free to make your own way back to where you live; *or*

■ an appointment will be made for you with an out-patient clinic – for example, for a further assessment, medical test or diagnosis; *or*

■ you will be admitted straight away for further hospital treatment.

Unlike A&E admissions – which might happen because of a medical emergency, such as someone falling over and breaking their arm or hip – elective surgery involves planned treatment. An example is having an operation to remove a cataract. This is also an example of a type of surgery that can often be done during the day (see page

165). This means you don't have to stay in overnight but can return home after a short rest.

## Targets

There are several targets about hospital treatment that you should know about. These apply whether or not you need to stay in hospital or have day surgery. From 1 April 2004 no one should wait for more than nine months for elective (planned) surgery. By December 2005, nobody should wait more than six months to go into hospital for treatment.

By 2008, there should be a maximum of 18 weeks between your GP referring you to hospital and the hospital providing the treatment you need. This 18-week period includes the hospital carrying out all the tests that might be needed to diagnose your condition. In the meantime, from the end of 2004 no NHS patient should wait more than nine months from being referred by their GP to necessary hospital treatment being carried out. Anyone waiting more than six months will be offered the choice of an alternative hospital for faster treatment (see Box 17).

By December 2005, you should not have to wait more than three months (13 weeks) for an out-patient appointment.

There are two targets for people with cancer. The first is that, if your GP suspects you have cancer, they can make an urgent referral to the local NHS cancer services. The referral is to find out whether you have cancer. If you are diagnosed with cancer, from December 2005 you should wait no longer than two months from the urgent referral being made to your receiving treatment for the cancer. The two-month period allows for the diagnosis to be confirmed – but if you are diagnosed with cancer, from December 2005 you should receive treatment for it no later than one month afterwards.

There is also a target about treatment for people with cataracts. Since the end of 2004, no one should wait more than three months for their cataract operation.

All these targets are set by the government of the day.

---

**Box 17. Choose and Book**

There is a target about your being able to choose the hospital where you receive your NHS care. There are two parts to this: the first is about choosing the hospital and the second is about making the appointment.

*Choosing the hospital*

The first part of Choose and Book is about having a choice of which hospital you might go to. Remember that this is about NHS care, so the hospital must be either an NHS Trust (or NHS Foundation hospitals) or private (or voluntary) health care provider that has a contract with the NHS for the particular treatment you need. Your GP will be able to advise you about choosing a hospital or treatment centre. The aim is that, by December 2005, all NHS patients in England will have the choice of four or five places for planned treatment (elective care). But you do not have to choose, if you don't want to. You can ask your GP to decide on your behalf.

*Booking an appointment*

By the end of 2005, the NHS must make sure that every hospital appointment booked is for the convenience of the patient.

In the past, GPs wrote a letter referring their patient to a particular hospital. Patients then received a letter from the hospital telling them the time and date to attend. Often, patients needed to change these appointments because they were inconvenient.

The idea now is to improve appointments through a new system called Choose and Book. This applies to appointments for in-patient care (where you stay overnight in hospital) as well as out-patient clinics. Day surgery arrangements are described on page 165.

Choose and Book means that, during a visit to your GP, you and your GP can book the hospital appointment together. This is done electronically, using computers at the GP's surgery. You and your GP will be able to see the dates and times available for you to choose from. Information about the booking can then be printed out for you to take away with you. This new system is being introduced throughout England during 2004–2005. It is planned to cover the whole of England by the end of 2005.

There will also be an option for you to make the appointment yourself, at home, either by telephone or by using the Internet if you have access to a computer. The GP will give you some Appointment Request information, which you will need before you contact the hospital. This information will include a reference number, and details of the hospital you and your GP have chosen. You will also need to agree a password with your GP and then tell this to the hospital when you contact it, so that hospital staff know they are making the appointment for the right person. You might want to make the appointment yourself if you need to ask relatives or friends about being away. For example, if you would need someone to take care of your pet while you were in hospital, you'd want to find out when the person who will do this will be free, before making the appointment.

You will also be able to change the appointment by telephone if something happens in the meantime to stop you going on the original date. You can do this whether you have made the booking yourself or the GP has made the appointment at the surgery.

If English is not your first language, when you contact Choose and Book you should say which language you would prefer to speak. Choose and Book will arrange for an interpreter on the telephone to help you.

More information about Choose and Book is on the website, www.chooseandbook.nhs.uk.

It is important to remember that the targets set out on pages 152–153 are all about NHS services. They don't apply to private health care treatments that you buy yourself in the UK. However, the targets do apply to private health care services that the NHS has agreed to pay for on your behalf. This is because, when the NHS pays, you 'count' as an NHS patient, even if the treatment is provided by a private health company.

# NHS health care given overseas

In some areas, and for a very small number of patients, the NHS has arranged for treatment to be carried out in a European Economic Area (EEA) country. This has been one of the ways in which the NHS has cut waiting lists for operations. These arrangements are made by local Primary Care Trusts.

Some criteria apply to overseas treatment paid for by the NHS. The first is that the clinic or hospital must provide a good-quality service. Another is that the patient must be well enough to travel (this must be no more than a three-hour flight from the UK). Follow-up checks and treatment are carried out in the UK. Because the NHS has arranged and paid for the treatment, everything (including the flight) is free for the patient. But if you wanted to take someone with you, and there was no medical reason for this, they would have to pay for their flight and accommodation. In any case, patients travel together in small groups, with at least one person (sometimes more, depending on patients' medical needs) from the NHS in support.

If you are offered overseas treatment paid for by the NHS, you do not have to accept. You can ask the NHS to arrange care for you in the UK, as usual. You can also ask your local Primary Care Trust to arrange overseas treatment for you, in an EEA country, but it does not have to agree to this. It is not clear, however, whether many Primary Care Trusts will be offering this option in the future, given that waiting times for many treatments have been reducing.

# Private health care

How quickly you receive private treatment depends on you and the particular clinic. Private and voluntary sector hospitals and clinics are regulated and inspected by the Healthcare Commission (see page 10). If you have complaints about the private health care treatment you have received, you can take this to the Healthcare Commission if you are unhappy with the response from the clinic or hospital (see page 10). You can also complain about individual health professionals to the relevant body that registers them (see Chapter 16).

If you receive private health care that then goes wrong and you go to the NHS with this problem, the NHS has the right to ask the private clinic to pay for the costs of the later NHS treatment.

## Consenting to treatment

As with all health care, you must agree to hospital treatment before it can go ahead. This is called *giving your consent*. You will be asked to sign a consent form, usually quite soon after you arrive in hospital. This sets out what you are agreeing to.

Sometimes, when you are given this, the doctor or nurse who gives it to you may be in a hurry. You may feel they want you to sign without reading the whole form. Don't be put off. If you want to read the whole form, no one should stop you or make you feel you are wasting time. Ask for a few minutes so you can read it properly. If the doctor or nurse is impatient, politely suggest they do something else for a couple of minutes while you read it.

If you come into hospital as the result of an accident, there may not be time for you to give consent, if emergency treatment is needed. Or you may come into hospital unconscious or unable to say what you want to happen. In such a situation, the hospital staff will do whatever is needed to save your life and stabilise your condition. But if you have a Living Will (also called an advance decision or advance directive) that sets out the treatments you do not want, this should be respected. There is more about this on page 126.

You may also have made an advance statement saying you want everything possible done to prolong your life – see page 129. If you have made one of these documents, you may want to think about whom you have told about it – there is no register as yet for advance decisions and advance statements. You could tell your GP and give them a copy but you may also want to tell people close to you, and possibly carry a copy with you.

---

**There is more about Living Wills in Age Concern Information Sheet IS5 *Advance Statements, Advance Directives and Living Wills*.**

---

You do not have to make either a Living Will or an advance statement. If you have any uncertainties about drawing up either of these documents, or you object for other reasons, you should not make one. The decisions that are made on your behalf must be in your 'best interests' – see Chapter 8 and Chapter 18.

People often think that, if a relative or their spouse or partner is taken into hospital and cannot consent to treatment, they will be asked to decide, as next of kin (Box 18). But the law is not so clear about this subject. There is no absolute right for you, as next of kin, to decide what should happen – but your opinion should be sought. At the moment, it is up to doctors to decide, together with the whole clinical team treating your relative.

If the medical decision is about withholding or withdrawing treatment, and you disagree with it because you think the person would disagree, you can go to the law courts to ask for a judgement. In the meantime, treatment should continue to be provided. There is more about this in Chapter 15.

**Box 18. Next of kin**

There is no absolute legal definition of who is your next of kin, but usually this is taken to mean either:

- your spouse (someone you are legally married to), *or*
- a close blood relative.

Problems can arise if, for example, you live with someone of the opposite sex as your partner but you are not married. Gay and lesbian couples will be able to officially cement their relationship through the local register office, under the Civil Partnerships Act 2004. Although the Act does not specifically set out 'next of kin' rights, it should help such couples in this respect.

You can also nominate your next of kin. When you go into hospital for planned treatment, you will almost certainly be asked to say who your next of kin is and to give their contact details. It is entirely up to you whom you choose, but make sure that the person knows they are listed in this way. Even if you are married and have children, if you feel closest to a cousin or a friend, you could decide to nominate that person as your next of kin. It really is up to you.

There are proposals in the Mental Capacity Bill to make it much clearer who can – and who cannot – make health care decisions on behalf of people who do not have the mental capacity to do this for themselves at the time (see page 123). But this is not yet the law. In the meantime, decisions follow the lines described above. See also Chapter 8.

After your treatment, hospitals will usually give only your family information about how things have gone. However, even though someone is part of your family, you may not want them to know about what is happening. You can always tell the ward staff whom they should, and should not, give out information to. They should respect your wishes. If they do give information to someone you have asked them not to, or refuse to give details to someone you have said must be told, you can make a complaint about this. (See Chapter 16.)

# Road traffic accidents

If you have NHS hospital treatment because you are the victim of a road traffic accident, and if you then go on to claim and receive personal injury compensation, the NHS has the right to pursue the insurer for the cost of your treatment. But you will not be asked to pay – the insurer pays the NHS's charges and the treatment is still free to you. There are plans to extend this arrangement to all personal injury compensation.

# Mixed wards

Most hospitals have been working for some years towards having single-sex wards – separate wards for men and for women. But mixed wards of both men and women still exist. If you would rather be on a single-sex ward, ask staff if it is possible. If this is important to you, it might be one of the questions you want answered before choosing one hospital over another for planned surgery.

# Hospital food

Attempts have been made over the past couple of years to improve hospital catering. Many catering services were contracted out to the private sector during changes to the NHS in the 1980s. This means that most of the food in hospitals is provided by private companies whose staff are not part of the NHS.

Good food is an important part of patients' health and recovery. Some hospitals assess patients to check whether they are poorly nourished, so that steps can be taken to improve their diet and overall health while in hospital. Some hospitals now offer a ward kitchen, where food can be available 24 hours a day rather than the fixed mealtimes usually offered.

Nurses and health care workers have been reminded of the importance of helping patients to eat – for example, taking the cling film off sandwiches or removing the foil lid from small pots of yoghurt.

If you have particular dietary needs – for whatever reason – be sure to tell the ward staff as soon as you can. If you know you are going into hospital and will be staying, ask your GP or your local Patient Advice and Liaison Service about letting them know in advance.

## Religious and spiritual needs

When we think about hospital services, most of us think about our physical health. But as individuals we may also have spiritual or religious needs. The Human Rights Act 1998 gives us all individual rights to religious observance. Respecting our religious beliefs is also one of the important principles of the NHS. It is found in the NHS Plan and in the various National Service Frameworks.

All NHS hospital Trusts must have a multi-faith facility. There should be a code of conduct on the sharing of 'sacred space' – this is usually a part of the hospital (eg a room) that is put aside to be used by patients of all denominations and religious beliefs.

This used to be called the hospital chaplain service. But you might find it is now called something like chaplainry and spiritual caregivers, or faith community representatives. This change is to represent the very wide range of faiths held by people living in the UK. Whatever it is called, you may well find that it is linked with the hospital Trust's bereavement service (see page 220).

## Telephone and TV

Many hospitals still have day rooms where you can sit and watch television or read. Most wards also have a payphone, or there will be one nearby. You will be asked not to use mobile phones in hospital – having these switched on can interfere with the smooth running of some hospital equipment, including health equipment used by other patients.

There is now a facility where you can arrange to have a telephone and TV by your bedside. Called Patient Power, it is run by private companies. You have to pay for this even if you are an NHS patient. There is usually a daily amount to pay to watch the television, and a charge for the phone calls that you make. People who phone you may find this costs them more than usual. But it is up to you whether you have this. If you do have it, make sure you know how much it will cost you and ask about the cost of calls made to you on this system.

Volunteers in many hospitals also run hospital radio services, which are free and available to all patients.

## Car parking

As with hospital catering services, many hospitals' car parking arrangements were contracted out to the private sector some years ago. Where this has happened, it means that it is not really up to the hospital how much it costs to park in the car park. It is up to the company that runs the car park.

Each hospital has its own arrangement, so there will be different amounts to pay depending where you are. If you are eligible for help with travel costs for health care, you can claim back the amount you have paid for car parking as well as any other travel costs. See page 95 for details of help with health costs.

## Visitors

Most wards have set times for visitors each day. If you know that someone you would like to visit you cannot come at those times because of other commitments that cannot be changed, ask the nurse in charge of the ward if they can come at another time. This is usually not a problem to arrange but they should check first. For example, some wards prefer not to allow visitors at certain mealtimes so that patients can concentrate on eating and staff can concentrate on helping them.

Remember that it is up to you whether you want to have visitors. If there are some people you don't want to see, tell them but also tell the ward staff. If they come anyway and you don't feel up to seeing them, ask them if they would mind leaving. If there are problems, ask the ward staff for help.

## Your money in hospital

People who receive some income from the state (often called state benefits) can find that this is affected if they are in hospital for any length of time. Such state benefits include:

- state retirement pension;
- Attendance Allowance;
- Pension Credit.

Patients who are not yet receiving state retirement pension may find that Incapacity Benefit or Jobseekers Allowance is also affected.

This overall policy of reducing state benefits while receiving NHS in-patient care dates back to the beginnings of the welfare state in

1948. But the detail of what is affected, by how much and at what stage has changed.

The current rules are different for the various benefits. For example, your state pension is reduced after you have been in hospital for 52 weeks. Pension Credit is also affected. Attendance Allowance (or Disability Living Allowance) will stop after you have been in hospital for 28 days but it will restart once you return home, provided you tell your local Pension Service office.

---

There is more about this in Age Concern's book *Your Rights*; and in Age Concern Factsheet 34 *Attendance Allowance and Disability Living Allowance* and Factsheet 48 *Pension Credit*.

---

Note that being in hospital doesn't affect any private income you have. Private income means any occupational pension (even if this comes from the public sector job you used to do) or private pension or money from investments (such as interest in savings, or dividends on stocks and shares). Any savings you have are not affected.

If you are a private patient and paying for your own hospital care, neither your state benefits nor any other income you receive is affected by your being in hospital (although in practice you may use some of your income to pay towards your bill).

## Your pet when you are in hospital

If you don't have someone to look after your pet while you are in hospital, the first thing to think about is whether you could board your cat in a cattery (or dog in kennels). There are also some places that will take rabbits, hamsters and budgerigars – even snakes. You can find these by looking in your local *Yellow Pages* or other telephone directory. You could also ask local animal welfare organisations for suggestions.

If there are problems, or you cannot afford the cost of the boarding arrangement, the charity the Cinnamon Trust might be able to help (contact details on page 268). It has a lot of volunteers working across the country, helping to look after the pets of older people and people with a terminal illness.

## Help you were already receiving

If you were already receiving some help before you went into hospital (such as personal care at home), you should tell the people who provide your care what is happening. If any of your support comes from social services, or if they help to organise this for you or pay towards the help you receive, you should also contact that department – or ask someone to do this on your behalf. Make sure that these arrangements are re-started, if needed, when you leave hospital (see Chapter 12).

## Day surgery

More surgery and treatment is being carried out during the day, without your needing to stay in hospital overnight. This is because improvements in some treatments make it safe for you to come into hospital in the morning, have an operation and return home later that day. Examples include eye surgery to remove cataracts and hernia repair. Even so, the hospital or clinic that carries out the treatment must be satisfied that you are well enough to leave before you are discharged. There is more about this in Chapter 12.

For the last couple of years there has been a booking system for day surgery along the lines described in Box 17 (page 153). Since March 2004, all appointments for day cases should be made in this way. This is also part of Choose and Book.

# Out-patient clinics

There are many different reasons why you might be asked to attend a hospital out-patient clinic or department. They include:

- to have your illness diagnosed;
- to receive the results of tests, and be told your diagnosis;
- to check whether surgery or a treatment has been successful;
- to monitor your progress;
- for particular help, such as speech and language therapy;
- to complete treatment – for example, by removing stitches from healed surgery wounds.

Depending on your health needs, you may also regularly attend a clinic or services such as one offering day support for people with dementia (see Chapter 8).

Before you are discharged from hospital, either as an in-patient or from an A&E unit, you may be told to make an out-patient appointment if this is needed (see Chapter 12).

## Moving between hospitals

If you need to move between one NHS hospital or clinic and another for medical reasons, the NHS will organise this. This might be in an ambulance, if you need this because of the condition of your health, or it could be in another vehicle that the ambulance service uses as part of its Patient Transport Service (PTS). (See also Chapters 2 and 13.)

## Leaving hospital

There has been a huge emphasis in recent years on issues about NHS patients needing to leave hospital (being discharged) much more quickly. This emphasis has come from lots of different sources, including various governments, media, health professionals and campaigning charities. This is discussed in Chapter 12.

## Chapter 12

# Coming out of hospital

This chapter looks at how your leaving NHS hospital – being discharged – should be handled. It covers the discharge process; discharging yourself; refusing to leave; and getting intermediate and ongoing care. It also describes the Single Assessment Process (SAP), discusses follow-up care and looks at what rights, if any, extend to private hospital patients.

You will also find a lot of helpful detail in Age Concern Factsheet 37 *Hospital discharge arrangements*.

## Planning ahead for discharge

All the advice to the NHS is that staff must plan ahead for your eventual discharge from hospital. This includes patients who are admitted following an emergency or accident.

Planning ahead is particularly important for patients who:

- Were already receiving some care and support before coming into hospital (eg having help at home or living in a care home).
- Are likely to need support for the first time as a result of whatever has happened to bring them into hospital (eg because of a stroke).

Several steps must be followed before these patients leave hospital, as explained below. If you were already receiving care at home before going into hospital, for example, you should make sure that this will start again on your return home, if it is still needed. If you cannot organise this yourself, ask the ward staff or any social services staff based at the hospital to help you (see page 170).

## If you are going back home

Many older patients go into hospital for surgery and treatment, and will not need further support after they have been discharged home. Even so, there may be items you need to take with you that should be ready for you before you are discharged. They include:

- any medication you now need to take (the hospital pharmacy usually issue you with a small amount to tide you over until you can get further supplies on prescription from your GP);
- details of any follow-up or out-patient clinic appointments;
- any advice about once you have left the hospital – such as about not getting any stitches wet.

You may also want to ask staff whom you should contact if you have any concerns about your treatment once you get home.

You may need someone to come and collect you from hospital, if you cannot make your own way home. Failing that, you may need to organise a taxi or find out if there are volunteer car drivers in your area who might take you to your home for a small charge. Or you may need an ambulance or Patient Transport Service (PTS) – for example, if you are leaving hospital with your leg in plaster and would not be able to get into an ordinary car. Ask the ward staff for help in arranging this. Helping you sort out transport should be part of the checklist that staff go through when drawing up a discharge plan for you before you leave hospital.

You might need some help when you first get home – for example, food shopping or laundry to be done. If you need help to make these sorts of arrangements before you leave hospital, ask the ward staff how they can help you. You should not be discharged from hospital until all the arrangements identified as needed in your discharge plan are in place.

---

Age Concern Factsheet 37 *Hospital discharge arrangements* has more information.

---

## If you need ongoing care

If any of the NHS staff involved in your care think you might need help to be organised or provided by social services for when you have left hospital, they must tell social services straight away. This involves either contacting the main social services department locally or getting in touch with social workers based at the hospital. Even though they may work in the hospital's building, these social workers are employed by the local authority social services.

The hospital staff should tell you that social services are being contacted. You can refuse help from social services – and you can refuse to speak to anyone from social services. Be aware, though, that many older people in need of ongoing support receive at least some of this via their local social services department.

When social services receive the referral, they must visit you in hospital within the next couple of days. They will work with the health staff as well as with you and any carer (eg a relative or friend) to find out what help you might need.

Since April 2004, this 'finding out' has been called the Single Assessment Process (SAP). One of the main ideas behind this Process is that, even though several different professionals may be involved in drawing up a full picture of your current situation and likely future needs, you shouldn't have to keep repeating the same information. Instead, with the Single Assessment Process, each time another professional is involved they should add to the overall picture.

Another major part of the Single Assessment Process is making sure that your views of your needs and circumstances are fully taken into account.

With your permission, information you give as part of the Single Assessment Process will be shared with other professionals who are either already involved in your care or might need to be involved once you leave hospital. If you have a carer, you need to agree to their views being sought.

Once an assessment has been completed, staff will look to see whether your needs will be met by either the NHS or social services. Before you leave hospital the hospital staff must look at whether your needs meet the criteria for continuing NHS health care services (see Chapter 13). Help from either the NHS or social services might include:

- NHS fully funded continuing health care (see page 187);
- intermediate care (see page 89);
- help at home arranged by social services;
- a place in a care home;
- a move to sheltered housing.

The NHS and social services set eligibility criteria for the support that each provides. These are 'rules' or measures against which your needs are compared. If your needs meet the criteria, you will be eligible for help and receive the relevant support. There is more about this in Chapter 13.

Once it has been agreed that some services will be provided for you, you should be given a care plan setting out what is needed, who will provide it and whether you will have to pay anything. Unlike the NHS, you will have to pay towards the costs of support from social services. How much you pay depends on the type of service. There are different rules depending on whether this will be care at home, a place in a care home, or an adaptation to your house or flat (eg fitting grab rails or a stairlift).

Further information about help from social services is available in the following Factsheets from Age Concern:

41 *Local authority assessment for community care services*

46 *Paying for care and support at home*

24 *Direct payments from social services*

10 *Local authority charging procedures for care homes*

Chapter 13 has more information about continuing NHS health care. If you are told you are not eligible for continuing NHS health care but you believe you meet the criteria, you have the right to ask for this decision to be reviewed. Ideally, you should do this before you are discharged. While the review is being carried out, you *should not* be discharged from hospital.

For more information, see Age Concern Factsheet 37 *Hospital discharge arrangements* and Factsheet 20 *Continuing NHS health care, NHS funded registered nursing care and intermediate care.*

# Being discharged

It is generally accepted that being in a hospital ward for a long time is not very good for you. Wards tend not to be either very stimulating or relaxing places to be. On the other hand, you should only be asked to leave hospital when it is clinically (medically) appropriate for you to do so. This means that the doctor in charge of your care (either the consultant or, sometimes, a GP in a community hospital) has to decide that you can now leave hospital.

You can also choose to discharge yourself, even if this is against the doctors' opinion. You will probably be asked to sign something to say that this is your decision and you understand what the consequences might be.

Every NHS hospital should have a discharge policy, and every ward should have a key discharge person who is able to tell you what will happen before and after you leave hospital. This includes information about any follow-up appointments you might need, perhaps at an out-patient clinic, together with supplies of any medicine you are to take in the immediate future (plus instructions on how to take it) or details of diet or exercise plans you should be following.

If staff can't give you any information about how discharge is handled at the hospital, you can ask the hospital's Patient Advice and Liaison Service (PALS) for help to find this out (see also Chapter 16).

If it has been agreed that you will be provided with care and support after you have left hospital, you should not be discharged until this is ready. It must be safe to discharge you – this means that whatever is needed next must be in place. If it is not, 'transitional' arrangements can be made. They can include:

- A temporary place in a care home – perhaps because the home you would like to go to has no vacancies at that time; or because adaptation work to your own home is too disruptive for you to be there while it is being carried out.
- A temporary stay in a sheltered housing scheme.

Or you might want to make your own temporary arrangements while everything is sorted out, perhaps staying with a relative or friend.

*173*

There is more information about moving to a care home after hospital in Age Concern Factsheet 29 *Finding care home accommodation*.

Another option might involve you moving temporarily to a different ward – perhaps from a specialist stroke ward to a general ward. This might also happen if you no longer needed the specialist stroke care but were not quite ready to be discharged from hospital.

Arrangements made by social services for you to receive help at home after being in hospital should be reviewed within two weeks of your returning home (and preferably within the first few days if you live alone). This review is to check that everything is working as it should be and to make sure that what is being provided meets your assessed needs.

If you are eligible for help from social services with the cost of a place in a care home (including a home that offers nursing care), social services should help you find somewhere suitable. However, if you will be paying privately, you (or someone on your behalf) may need to make these arrangements yourselves.

See Age Concern Factsheet 29 *Finding care home accommodation*; Factsheet 10 *Local authority charging procedures for care homes* explains the system of state support from social services. You could also contact Age Concern's helpline or the charity Counsel and Care (address on page 270) for advice and information on finding and paying for a care home.

You can, of course, refuse any of the help you are offered. There are a few circumstances where you would have to accept care and support – these are described in Chapter 8. But even if you do refuse the help on offer for when you leave hospital, this doesn't mean you can stay in the hospital indefinitely.

If any part of your discharge is handled poorly, you can use the NHS complaints system if your complaint is about the hospital or its staff (see Chapter 16); or if you have a complaint about social services, you can use the local authority's complaints system.

This is explained in Age Concern Factsheet 41 *Local authority assessment for community care services.*

# Refusing to leave hospital

Sometimes NHS patients refuse to leave hospital at the point they are told they have been discharged. There is usually one of two reasons for this:

■ The patient doesn't agree that they are clinically fit to leave. They believe that further treatment is needed in hospital.

■ The patient refuses to accept the arrangements being proposed for them once they have been discharged. This is often when either: the assessment is for a place in a care home but the person believes they could manage at home (albeit with some support); or they understand they will be moving to a care home but there is nothing suitable with a vacancy.

In the first situation, you should make sure that the ward staff and the consultant in charge of your care understand your concerns. You could ask the hospital's Patient Advice and Liaison Service to get involved and help you sort this out (see page 228). You may want to ask for a second opinion (see page 40). You might also find it helpful to talk to a charity that specialises in the health condition that is being treated at the time (see the Appendix for examples). It may be able to shed further light on whether anything else should or could be done at that hospital at that time.

In the second situation, it's really important for you to know that:

■ The hospital must have a policy – a written document – that sets out what action it will take in these situations. You should ask for a copy.

■ You cannot be forced to go into a care home except in very extreme circumstances (see Chapter 8). You can ask social services to come up with alternatives – but if you refuse all reasonable options (and you have been asked about these more than once), social services can decide it has met its duty in law to provide support. In that case, everyone may be asking you to make your own arrangements.

Nevertheless, it's equally important that you don't feel pressured or even bullied into doing something that will be wrong for you. Moving into a care home is a major decision. There is a lot of focus (shared by all governments since the early 1990s) on people being supported to stay at home for as long as possible. If you think you could manage at home, ask social services and the NHS about what it can do to help support you at home or in a sheltered flat, perhaps on a temporary or short-term basis just for everyone to see what is really possible and whether it will work. Ask about the rehabilitation and intermediate care services that are available in your area. If, in the end, you decide to move into a care home, do bear in mind that many people enjoy living there.

Even if the NHS has bought your care from a private hospital, the NHS remains responsible for handling your discharge from hospital.

## Private patients

Things are a little different if you are paying privately for your hospital treatment. Most people pay for private health care by either:

- a private health insurance policy; *or*
- paying in full for the cost of each treatment.

If you stay longer than your insurance policy allows, your insurer may ask you to pay for any extra costs. The basic rule of thumb is that the longer you stay, the bigger your bill is likely to be. If the private hospital doesn't believe you have either the money or the intention to pay for the bill, it may insist that you leave.

If, following your private treatment, you will need ongoing care, you should first talk to the hospital staff and your private health care insurer (if you have one) about what might be needed. Even if you are a private patient, you are still eligible for ongoing support from the NHS and social services. Bear in mind that the emphasis on reducing delayed discharges applies to patients who are being discharged from NHS beds. But you should still contact social services and ask them to assess your needs as quickly as possible.

The private hospital might also refer your case to the NHS for ongoing support. It might do this if, for example, you unexpectedly need rehabilitation services that it cannot provide.

# Chapter 13

# NHS care where you live

This chapter describes two different types of NHS entitlement. The first part looks at your rights to NHS services depending on the level of your care needs. This considers the rights of people living in care homes (with or without nursing care) or sheltered housing to NHS services. It also looks at the system of continuing NHS health care for people with ongoing and often serious health problems and/or high levels of health care needs.

The second part looks at your rights to the NHS if you are away from where you usually live, including when you are temporarily away from home but still in the UK and if you normally live abroad but are taken ill on a visit to the UK. This also explains the differences for UK citizens who live in EU (European Union) and non-EU countries.

## People who live in a care home or sheltered housing

No matter where you live, you may still need the services of a GP and a dentist, among other NHS professionals.

If you live in a care home (a home registered to give you personal care but not nursing care) or in sheltered housing (whether you own or rent this), you have exactly the same rights to the NHS as if you were still living in your own home. This includes:

■ being registered with a GP – but you may find that you are taken on by a different practice, if by moving to live in a care home or sheltered flat you leave your previous surgery's area;
■ being registered as an NHS patient with a dentist;
■ district nursing services;
■ free NHS hearing tests;
■ access to free NHS hospital treatment.

If you are aged 60 or over and live in any type of care home, you are also still entitled to:

■ free NHS prescriptions;
■ free NHS eyesight tests.

You may also be eligible for particular types of NHS care called continuing NHS health care. This is explained below. It includes continence advice and pads, and some transport to and from hospitals and clinics. There are also some reductions in the cost of NHS dentistry and optical services. You may also be able to get some help with equipment (see page 100).

The Department of Health's leaflet HC11 *Help with health costs* explains about reduced charges for some NHS dentistry and optical services (see page 92).

If you live in a care home and pay towards this cost (with or without help from social services), you should have a contract with the home that sets out the support the home provides that you have to pay towards. If this includes services you believe should be available from the NHS, you can:

■ ask the home to arrange these for you;

- contact your local Patient Advice and Liaison Service for advice (see Chapter 16).

If you believe you are being asked to pay for services that the NHS is either already providing free of charge to the care home or should be providing, you can complain to the Commission for Social Care Inspection (CSCI), which inspects and registers care homes (see page 269).

---

Age Concern Factsheet 29 *Finding care home accommodation* and Factsheet 44 *NHS services and older people* may also be helpful.

---

# People living in nursing homes

There is one major difference between those living in care homes and those living in homes registered to provide nursing services (nursing homes) in England in terms of access to NHS services. This is about how the nursing elements of your care are provided.

Instead of providing you with NHS district nursing services, the NHS makes a payment to the home for the nursing care you need and which the home provides. This system is called *registered nursing care contribution* (RNCC). The payment is made by your Primary Care Trust covering the part of the country where you live in the home. There are other parts of your care that you will have to pay for, though, including food, accommodation and personal care. Although you should not also pay the home for the RNCC, the home can either:

- charge you for the entire cost of all the care it provides, then give you the money for the RNCC it receives from the NHS for you; *or*
- charge you for everything it provides *except* the amount of the RNCC it receives for you.

However this is paid, you should be told exactly how the RNCC payment affects your fees.

There are some limits as to what the RNCC covers. The first is that it applies only to care provided direct by a registered nurse or to the time he or she takes to delegate or supervise care carried out by another worker (such as a care assistant). It does not cover the care provided by that delegated worker. Chapter 3 explains how trained nurses are registered.

The second limit is that an RNCC assessment must be carried out before the NHS will make the payment. Just because you live in a nursing home doesn't mean you automatically qualify – an assessment must be carried out.

Before an RNCC assessment is made, however, your care needs should first be assessed jointly by the NHS and social services. If you have recently moved to a nursing home for the first time, the assessment should have happened before you moved into the home; but if you have lived in a nursing home for some years and been paying for this yourself, an assessment may not have been carried out recently. The health and social services assessment should also look at whether you are entitled to continuing NHS health care (see page 183). Only when this assessment has concluded that you should be living in a nursing home but you are not eligible for continuing NHS health care will a RNCC assessment be carried out.

If you are not sure what assessments have been carried out, start by asking the manager of the home where you are living. They should tell you if and when an assessment has been done, and whom to contact in the NHS or social services if this has not happened. Otherwise, you could contact your local Primary Care Trust and ask that both the continuing NHS health care *and* the RNCC assessments be carried out. Once the assessment has been carried out, you should be told it has been done, what the outcome (result) is, and how to appeal against the decision if you think this is wrong.

A nurse employed by the Primary Care Trust will carry out the RNCC assessment. They will look at your needs as an individual, bearing in mind that care needs can vary over several days or weeks. Once the assessment is completed, the Primary Care Trust decides whether the amount and type of nursing care you need to receive in the home falls into one of three 'bands':

- **Low band** – £40 per week. This applies if your nursing care needs can be met with minimal registered nurse input.
- **Medium band** – £77.50 per week. To fit this band, you will have multiple (several) care needs. A registered nurse will need to provide care to you on at least a daily basis. Although you may need access to a nurse at any time, your condition is stable and predictable and likely to remain so provided that your current treatment and care arrangements continue.
- **High band** – £125 per week. This applies if you have complex needs that require frequent attention by a registered nurse throughout a 24-hour period, and your physical/mental state is unstable and/or unpredictable.

Although the government sets these three bands, your Primary Care Trust can vary the amount it pays in your particular case. It can do this if, for example:

- Your needs are assessed as somewhere between the low and the medium bands.
- Your needs exceed the high band but still do not meet local criteria for fully funded continuing NHS health care. In this case you should ask for an explanation, and challenge the decision if you disagree with it – see page 188. You may also want to check whether you qualify for continuing health care if you have been placed in either the high or medium bands).

If you pay privately for your nursing home care and don't want the NHS to contribute to the costs of your care, you have the right to refuse this funding.

The system described above applies only to England. There are different arrangements in Scotland, Wales and Northern Ireland. The amounts for each band were last changed on 1 April 2005. Unlike state benefits, however, these amounts may not increase every year. To check if amounts have been increased, you can contact Age Concern's Information Line (see page 264).

Further details are in Age Concern Factsheet 20 *Continuing NHS health care, NHS funded registered nursing care and intermediate care.*

Apart from this RNCC system, you have the same entitlements to other NHS services as if you were still living at home. This includes access to NHS ambulance services because of an emergency admission to hospital from the home, or non-emergency transport to and from health care facilities. Such transport is part of the arrangements for continuing NHS health care services. It is often called Patient Transport Services (PTS) and is part of the service provided by Ambulance Trusts (see Chapter 2).

## Continuing NHS health care

For many years there have been concerns about what some see as an artificial 'line' between the care from social services and that provided by the NHS. One of the reasons this is important is that people have to pay from their income and savings towards social services' care, whereas most NHS care is provided free.

'Continuing NHS health care' is not the same thing as 'continuing care'. This might sound pedantic but it's important to know that these terms mean different things. *Continuing care* simply means you – or someone you know – has an ongoing (or continuing) condition or disability or illness. You, or they, will continue to need some kind of support or treatment. This might come from lots of different sources – some from the NHS, some from social services, perhaps some bought privately or some unpaid because it comes from friends and family. *Continuing NHS health care* is quite different. It doesn't describe your situation, it describes particular services that the NHS either pays for or provides itself.

Continuing NHS health care is one area where investigations by the Health Service Ombudsman (see Chapter 16) and case law (see Chapter 1) have had an important impact. They have helped to ensure that the NHS does provide certain types of support that, over many years, had been reducing. This includes:

- Continuing NHS health care in a care home or other setting, that the NHS pays for in full.
- Rehabilitation and recovery services (such as physiotherapy).
- Palliative care (this is for people whose life-threatening disease no longer responds to treatment).
- Respite health care (social services can also provide ordinary respite care – but you may be asked to pay towards this).
- Specialist health care support and advice (such as advice for diabetic care or stoma care, and specialist medical advice or treatment).
- Specialist health care equipment (such as continence pads and equipment to help prevent pressure sores).
- Specialist nursing and medical equipment (such as artificial feeding equipment that is normally available only in hospitals).
- Specialist transport (such as ambulances) to and from specific health care treatment (eg in hospital or a hospice) if this transport is required because of your medical condition.

# How do I get this?

Your health needs have to be assessed against criteria for different continuing NHS health care services. These criteria are a set of 'standards' or 'measures' – people whose health needs 'match' these measures will receive continuing NHS health care. So the main question is not *are* you ill or disabled but what does this mean you *need*?

There are 28 sets of criteria in England. They are drawn up separately by each of the 28 Strategic Health Authorities (StHAs – see page 2). But all 28 sets must be based on national guidance. The part of England covered by each Strategic Health Authority is quite large and so includes a number of different local authorities. Strategic Health Authorities have to agree their criteria with the local authorities in their area. This is because there can be overlaps between continuing NHS health care and what the local authorities' social services departments provide. They need to agree who pays for what.

Although the Strategic Health Authority agrees the criteria, the services provided to people meeting these criteria are paid for by the Primary Care Trust in which the person lives. The local Primary Care Trust is also responsible for making sure that your health needs are assessed, in order to compare these with the criteria that apply in your area. In December 2004 the Government commissioned a new national framework for assessing fully funded continuing NHS health care, although it was not clear at the time of writing when this might come into effect. Contact Age Concern Information Line (page 264) for further details.

Professionals with skills and knowledge relevant to your medical condition should be involved in your assessment. If you think you may be eligible for any continuing health care service because of the state of your health or disability, you can request an assessment. There are also times when an assessment must be carried out, including:

- when you are about to be discharged from hospital;
- when the annual review of your Registered Nursing Care Contribution (RNCC) is carried out (or sooner if your health gets significantly worse and you are already living in a care home registered to provide nursing care);
- if your health gets significantly worse and your current care package, regardless of where you are currently living, seems inadequate;
- if you have a terminal illness.

You might also want to ask for your health care needs to be assessed (or reassessed – it can be done more than once) if you live in a care home that isn't registered to provide nursing care but you are receiving intensive support from the district nursing service on a continual basis because you have a complex or unstable medical condition. Even if you are living at home and a relative and/or home care staff from a private agency or social services provide your care, you may be eligible for fully funded continuing NHS health care if your health needs are extremely high (psychological as well as physical health). This can be provided to support you to remain living at home.

---

Age Concern Factsheet 20 *Continuing NHS health care, NHS funded registered nursing care and intermediate care* has further details on this aspect.

---

A report from the Health Service Ombudsman, also published in December 2004 and drawing on details from almost 4,000 complaints made by members of the public on this issue, highlights the need for sufficient skilled assessors. She has made a number of recommendations for change but the Government had not yet responded at the time of going to press. To find out about any changes since the publication of this book, contact Age Concern's Information Line (page 264).

## Fully funded continuing NHS health care

In order for all your care to be funded by the NHS, your assessment must conclude that your main need (sometimes called your primary need) is for health care. Even if you also need other support such as help with accommodation and personal care (such as bathing) these may be secondary to your needs for health care. This can include your psychological (or mental) health as well as physical health.

When the NHS agrees to fund *all* the care you need, this is called 'fully funded continuing NHS health care'. This can be provided in your own home, in a nursing home or in a long-stay NHS facility.

A report from the Health Service Ombudsman in 2003 highlighted this issue for people in care homes. As a result, all Strategic Health Authorities and Primary Care Trusts have been required to check whether people in care homes (including nursing homes) in their area were wrongly denied access to fully funded NHS care. They have had to review all the cases already brought to their attention and also take steps to identify other cases that might have arisen, going back to 1996.

In some instances the NHS has now found that people were wrongly charged for their care in a home when the NHS should have paid for it. In these cases the NHS is reimbursing the amount those people have spent on their care. This includes people who have since died – it is being paid to their estate. While they were paying this charge themselves, people might have used their state benefits (eg Attendance Allowance) for it. When the NHS pays for care in full (as it does for people staying in NHS hospitals, for example), state benefits are reduced over time (see page 163). But because people were paying by mistake, the Government has told the Pensions Service (part of the Department for Work and Pensions, DWP) not to ask for these state benefits to be repaid when the person receives the NHS funds.

The Government has also told the NHS that, when someone's health needs are assessed for continuing NHS health care services, the decision must be recorded in his or her medical notes. They must also be told how they can ask for the decision to be reviewed. Primary Care Trusts and NHS Trusts also have new responsibilities about how assessments for continuing NHS health care services should be handled before patients are discharged from NHS hospital care. But your needs for continuing NHS health care can be assessed wherever you are – at home, in a care home, in sheltered housing; you don't have to be in hospital for this to happen. An example of why this assessment might be requested is the worsening of an illness or disability of someone already living in a care home but who does not need to be admitted to hospital.

---

**There is much more information in Age Concern Factsheet 20** *Continuing NHS health care, NHS funded registered nursing care and intermediate care*. **The Alzheimer's Society (contact details on page 265) also has further information.**

---

## Appealing against continuing NHS health care decisions

If you disagree with the decision about continuing NHS health care (including disagreeing with the nursing 'band' allocated to you following a reassessment under the Registered Nursing Care Contribution arrangements), you have the right to an independent review. You need to write to the Strategic Health Authority that issued the eligibility criteria used in your case and request an independent review.

An independent review will be done only if you are unhappy about:

- the procedures followed by the Primary Care Trust in deciding whether you meet the eligibility criteria;
- how the criteria have been applied in practice.

If you are unhappy about the criteria themselves (eg you think they are more strict than the government's guidance requires), you should pursue this through the NHS complaints system – see Chapter 16. An independent review cannot be used for this purpose.

Once it has received your request, the Strategic Health Authority decides whether to convene a review panel. It does not have to do this. For example, if your health needs fall well short of the criteria, it is extremely unlikely that the panel will meet. Even so, you should be told why a review panel is not going to be called to look at your appeal. You can use the NHS complaints system to complain about this decision not to convene a panel (see Chapter 16).

If a panel is convened, the aim is to complete the review within two weeks. If you are in hospital, you have the right to stay there until the review is concluded.

Although the review panel's decision is not binding, the expectation is that it will be followed. Once the decision has been made, you should be told this in writing. If you disagree with the panel's decision, you can go on to use the NHS complaints system. In this case, once a review panel has heard your appeal, you can take the matter direct to the Health Service Ombudsman rather than having to go through the earlier steps of the complaints system (see page 232).

---

Age Concern Factsheet 20 *Continuing NHS health care, NHS funded registered nursing care and intermediate care* has more information.

---

## Illnesses and accidents when you are away

## Visiting another part of the UK

If you are taken ill or have an accident while visiting another part of the UK, you are of course entitled to NHS services as usual.

There is, however, one difference in situations where you now need permanent care (perhaps in a care home or your own home) because of the illness or accident that occurred during your trip. This is because there are different systems of long-term care support for people who usually live in England, Wales, Northern Ireland or Scotland. If you will be returning to another part of the UK (your home area), you will need to make sure that whoever assesses your care needs understands this.

Sometimes, if you will need care from social services, someone from your local social services department will travel to where you are in hospital and assess your needs there. If you need to be moved to another hospital, or to a care home, and your medical condition is such that you can't travel by ordinary transport, the NHS where you are will arrange to transport you to the new facility. Unless you are being moved because of an emergency (eg if you need to go immediately to a more specialised NHS unit, because of a sudden change in your condition), the local Patient Transport Service (PTS – usually part of the local Ambulance Service) will provide transport.

There is more about help from social services in Age Concern Factsheet 6 *Finding help at home* and Factsheet 41 *Local authority assessments for community care services.*

# UK citizens visiting abroad

The European health insurance card is being introduced for UK citizens to prove their entitlement to health care services in countries with which the UK government has a reciprocal health agreement. They will be available in the UK by December 2005. Until then, you should still complete the E111 form as previously. These are available from post offices in the booklet *Health Advice for Travellers*.

The cards do not hold any information about medical treatment you have received but they will contain such details as your date of birth and name. They are valid only in EU countries.

If you visit other countries, especially those without a reciprocal health care arrangement, you should make sure you have sufficient appropriate private insurance. Even with E111 arrangements, though, it is still advisable to have holiday insurance that covers health care.

# Non-UK citizens on holiday in the UK

If you are a citizen of an EEA (European Economic Area) country, or of Switzerland, and you are taken ill while on a visit to the UK, you are entitled to reciprocal arrangements made between your government and that of the UK. This means that you are entitled to receive the same NHS care as those who live in the UK. Hospitals and GP surgeries can ask you to provide proof that you are visiting the UK from a country with which the UK government has a Bilateral Healthcare Agreement. It is for you to decide what to supply, but examples include:

■ passport or identity card;
■ travel documents;
■ a valid form E111, E110, E119 or E128;
■ a new European health insurance card.

The European health insurance card is being introduced across the EU (European Union), and will replace E111 and similar forms. Some countries began issuing these cards from 1 June 2004. In the UK, these cards must be in place by December 2005.

## UK citizens who live abroad

Many people believe that, because they are UK citizens, they are entitled to all NHS care even though they no longer live in the UK. They may think that, because they paid taxes and National Insurance contributions while they lived in the UK, this has somehow 'bought' them an entitlement for life. This is not the case.

Our rights to receive NHS treatment are limited by where in the world we are living at the time of needing NHS care.

This fact affects some older people who have decided to retire to live abroad. If your move is permanent, you are considered not to live in the UK any more – you now live in your adopted country (eg France or Spain). You may still visit the UK but, because you don't live here any more, you are regarded as a visitor. This gives you fewer rights to NHS services than people who do live here permanently.

There are some exemptions to this rule that apply *only* to people over the age of 60. One allows people who are still permanently living in the UK and spend *at least* six months out of every twelve here to be able to spend up to six months in an EEA (European Economic Area) country and not lose their full entitlement to NHS services. This exemption does not apply if you spend more than six months away from the UK in an EEA country. If you spend time visiting non-EEA countries (eg the USA), the six-month period does not apply; instead, you can keep your entitlement to NHS services only if you are out of the UK in non-EEA countries for fewer than three months. These times don't have to be over a calendar year – they are taken as three months or six months out of the twelve months before you needed the NHS treatment.

The NHS can ask you to prove your entitlement to NHS services. You would need to show evidence that you do live in the UK permanently.

## Health records if you move abroad

When you leave the UK to move abroad, your GP surgery sends the records they have kept to the local Primary Care Trust for storage. If you have had any hospital treatment, these records remain at the hospital or in a local archive. Hospital records are kept for at least eight years following the end of treatment. GP records are kept for at least ten years. At the end of these times, it is up to the Records Manager at the Primary Care Trust, hospital or archive to decide whether to continue to keep the records or destroy them.

You cannot take your records with you when you leave the UK but you may apply for copies, which you will have to pay for. You can take these copies with you. (The system of accessing copies of your records is explained in Chapter 17.)

## Health treatment if you live overseas

When you move to live abroad, you should make sure you know about that country's health services. The UK has reciprocal arrangements for its citizens with EEA (European Economic Area) countries, as well as Switzerland. This means that you have the same entitlement to that country's health services as do the citizens of that country who also live there permanently. But that country's system may be quite different from what is available through the NHS. For example, if you now live in Spain you will be entitled to the same Spanish health system as Spanish citizens; it does not mean that the Spanish system will deliver NHS care.

There are many countries, however, that do not have a reciprocal arrangement; the USA, for example. In those countries, you will probably have to pay for that country's health care services yourself, whether through relevant private health insurance schemes, from your savings, or via other private arrangements.

## Treatment on visits back to the UK

If you live abroad but are taken ill on a visit to the UK, there are some NHS services you can receive free of charge. These include:

- Services received in hospital accident and emergency (A&E) departments, Walk-In Centres and other units providing A&E-type treatments. (It does *not*, however, include the cost of any in-patient care or out-patient clinics attended following A&E care – such as surgery, for example.)
- Emergency treatment at a GP surgery.
- Compulsory psychiatric treatment.

There are also exemptions relating to family planning services, and treatment for certain illnesses on public health grounds.

If the care you need goes beyond these categories, the NHS can and will ask you to pay. The NHS can also ask you to pay if you visit the UK with a pre-existing condition (perhaps in the hope of receiving free treatment).

Even if you live abroad, however, you would be able to receive NHS services as usual in England if you are taken ill on a visit to the UK and receive either:

- UK War Disablement Pension; *or*
- UK War Widows Pension.

You might also be asked for proof that you receive these pensions – for example, your pension book or slip, or a letter from the Ministry of

Defence (MoD) or Department for Work and Pensions (DWP) stating that you receive one of these benefits. But you would still have to pay for any of the NHS services for which there is normally a charge (for example, NHS dentistry).

## Returning permanently to the UK

If you have lived abroad but are now returning to live in the UK, you will be entitled to the same NHS care as everyone else who lives here from the moment you arrive back in the UK. But you may well find that the NHS (eg a GP surgery) will ask for proof that you are now living here permanently. It is up to you what documents you provide in support of this, because ultimately it is up to you to prove you are living here permanently again: it is *not* up the NHS to do this. Examples of proof include bank statements showing withdrawals of money ending in one country and beginning in the UK, or details of travel documents.

If proposals to introduce a national identity card do eventually go ahead, you may be asked to provide this to prove your entitlement to NHS services. This could apply to everyone in the UK.

Age Concern Information Sheet IS2 *Information for older people moving back to the UK* may be helpful.

## Non-UK citizens who live in the UK

Although the rules for non-UK citizens vary depending on whether or not you are here working or studying, for example, the same broad rule of thumb about living here permanently applies. If you are entitled to live in the UK and you have made this your permanent home, you have the same rights to NHS services as everyone else who lives here.

Information on the entitlement of overseas visitors to free NHS treatment is available from the Department of Health (contact details on page 270).

# Chapter 14

# Organ and blood donation

This chapter looks at different ways of donating, including being a blood donor, and donating tissue, organs and bone marrow. It discusses being a 'living donor' as well as donating tissues and organs after death, including donating your body to medical science. It also looks at your rights to be a donor, to receive a donation and to refuse donations.

Sometimes organs and tissues might be retained after a post-mortem examination after you have died – this is not the same thing as organ donation. There is more about this in Chapter 15.

## Blood donors

The National Blood Service (NBS) runs the blood donor system for the NHS across the UK. Sessions are often run in doctors' surgeries or from mobile clinics put up for a few days in town hall car parks or other locations.

There is an upper age limit for people who give blood. This is 60 if you have never given blood before, but if you are already a regular donor you can continue to give blood up to the age of 70. This is not the only part of the system of donation where there is an upper age limit. Bone marrow donors can only do so up to the age of 44.

There are no age restrictions on who can *receive* blood, however – although you can refuse to receive blood (see page 202). No one receives payment for the blood they give to the NHS but, if you give blood, it will be tested and you will be told your blood type. If you are fit and healthy, you can give blood every six months. It is up to you whether you do this – no one can force you to give blood. To find out more, and to register to become a donor, get in touch with the National Blood Service (contact details on page 279).

# Tissue and organ donation

When we think about 'donors', we tend to think about blood donors and about donating organs such as heart, kidney and liver. But it is also possible to donate human tissue such as skin, bone and heart valves. The National Blood Service also runs a tissue donation programme, through NBS Tissue Services.

Some of these can be donated while you are still alive. For example, if you are having a hip replaced, you may be asked whether you would agree to donate any of the hip bone to other patients – perhaps someone who needs a bone graft because of disease or accident. You don't have to wait to be asked – you can offer this. Speak to the doctor or nurse in charge of your care at the time but make sure this is arranged before the operation takes place. It is also possible to donate some organs while you are alive. A good example of this is kidney donation. But the risk to you must be low, and you should not be pressured into doing this in any way – it must be voluntary on your part. You don't have to be related to someone for a transplant to work.

If you are a 'live' donor, the NHS can (but does not have to) reimburse you for any expenses relating to the operation such as travel, or loss of earnings if you are still working. Ask the NHS hospital where the transplant is to take place whether they might be able to help you with any expenses.

Tissue donation may also take place after a donor has died. Tissues can be successfully donated up to 24 hours after someone's heart has stopped beating. Some tissues, such as heart valves and corneas, can be successfully donated up to 72 hours after death.

As with blood and organs, you have to agree to donate tissue. You can do this either by carrying a donor card or by registering with the organ donor scheme (Box 19). It is worth telling your spouse or partner, and other family and friends, that you want to donate tissues and organs (and which ones – you can choose to donate some organs or tissues but not others) so that they can alert doctors to this fact at the time of your death.

Some doctors are understandably reluctant to ask families about donation when someone dies. But the nature of donation means that these questions have to be asked at this difficult time. If you are asked about donating the organs of someone you love who has just died or is dying, try to remember that the person asking isn't doing this to upset you. They are asking because of the patients who might be helped as a result of the donation.

But you should also not feel bad about saying no. If the person who has died didn't want to donate organs or tissues, everyone will understand the refusal. Just occasionally a family will refuse organ donation even though the person had an organ donor card and had already told them they wanted to donate organs in the event of their death. At present, although there is nothing in the law that requires doctors and the transplant service to find out what friends and family want, this is felt to be good practice. In the event that your family wanted to over-ride your wishes to donate, it is likely that the NHS would accept the family's view.

---

### Box 19. The Organ Donor Scheme

Most people are familiar with the organ donor card and many people carry one with them in their purse or wallet. You can also register with the National Organ Donor Register scheme. Hospitals can search the Register to see whether you had decided to donate organs, so they can let your family know about your wishes. Not everyone is comfortable talking about this in advance, especially if it is known that you are very ill and perhaps near death. People often prefer not to have to think about what might come next – this might be just as true for you as it is for your family or your friends.

You can contact the NHS Organ Donor Register or the British Organ Donor Society (BODY); their addresses are on pages 279 and 267.

---

You have the right to chose whether to be an organ or tissue donor. Indeed, if you are *not* registered with the organ donor scheme, and your family refuse permission, organs will not be taken. If you are not capable of deciding, or to say what your choice would be (perhaps you are in a coma), someone else can decide that your organs should not be donated. See also Chapter 8 for more information about people who lack the mental capacity to make decisions.

Your age doesn't affect whether your organs would be accepted. The important factor is their condition – age doesn't always affect this, especially in terms of organs such as corneas (from your eyes). If you die in hospital, it is possible that all your organs could be removed and used provided they are sufficiently healthy and you have given permission. If you die at home, though, usually only the corneas can be used.

If you are a donor, you cannot attach conditions to your donation, although people sometimes try. If you try to say you want your organs or blood or tissues to go to a woman, or a child, or to specify age or religion or anything else, your donation may be refused. The NHS is quite within its rights to refuse such donations. So if you agree to donate, you must understand that you have no say over who receives this.

## Receiving a donation

Everyone who is entitled to receive NHS care has the same rights to receive a donated organ, tissue or blood. This right is irrespective of whether they are being treated in NHS facilities at the time. Even if you are a private hospital patient, if you are entitled to NHS treatment, you could be offered a donated organ through the NHS service, which is run by a UK-wide part of the NHS called United Kingdom Transplant.

Note that seeking private treatment in the UK does not help you receive a transplant any faster. *All* transplants in the UK are handled through the NHS. This is because it is illegal to pay anyone to donate an organ or to receive payment for making a donation.

The details of everyone who is entitled to NHS treatment and needs a transplant are held on a database. This means that, as soon as an organ becomes available, the best possible clinical 'match' can be found as quickly as possible. There is also an agreed formula that decides which patient is top of the list at any one time. This varies according to the type of organ involved. For example, for kidney transplants there is a points system that takes into account the patient's tissue type, their time on the waiting list and any previous transplants as well as how far they are geographically from the donor.

If someone who is not entitled to NHS treatment needs a transplant in the UK, they will be offered the organ or tissue only if there is no one listed on the UK database who provides a 'match'.

If they wish, your family can be given some details such as the age, gender and family circumstances of the person or people who have benefited from the donation. The patient(s) who receive the organs can also receive similar details about the donor. Families can choose to exchange letters of thanks or good wishes through the transplant co-ordinator but these are anonymous. Sometimes it is possible for the donor's family to meet the person who has received an organ but both sides must agree; this too would be arranged through the transplant co-ordinator. You do not have the right to be told the name or address or other identifying facts about the people who receive donations from someone close to you.

## Refusing transplants and blood transfusions

Just as with any medical treatments, you may refuse a transplant and/or a blood transfusion. There are many reasons why someone might want to refuse, although perhaps the best known is refusing on the grounds of religious beliefs. Although most of the major world religions find the donating and receiving of organs, tissues and blood acceptable within their belief systems, Jehovah's Witnesses hold a strong belief against accepting blood transfusions if this involves blood from another person. However, some Jehovah's Witnesses will accept what is called auto-transfusion. This takes place during surgery, and involves any blood you lose during the operation being returned to you immediately.

If you would want to refuse a transplant or blood transfusion, you might find it helpful to carry a personal advance directive card or Living Will that says this (see also Chapter 8). Some hospitals also have forms that you can fill in to record your refusal of blood.

If you are involved in an accident and are brought to the hospital unconscious, staff will do their best to find out if you would refuse blood or other treatments. If you do not have anything on you that says so, and if staff can't get hold of someone quickly enough who would know your views and beliefs, they may go ahead with such treatments. This is because their over-riding responsibility is to preserve life where possible. Unless they know differently about you, they may administer blood products if these are needed. In these circumstances, it would be difficult for you to succeed in any claim of assault or injury you wanted to bring.

## Donating your body to medical science

Some people would like their body to be used for research or teaching purposes after their death. There are some circumstances where your body would not be accepted. These include if it has undergone a post-mortem examination or if organs (excluding corneas) have been donated.

You are advised to make your arrangements about this before your death, rather than leaving it to the person who will administer your estate (the Executor of your Will). Not all medical schools are looking for cadavers (corpses) at any one time, and if you've not already made an agreement, your Executors may find that no one will accept the body.

Arrangements in England, Wales and Scotland to donate the whole body for research, or for anatomical examination, can be made through Her Majesty's (HM) Inspector of Anatomy. People in Northern Ireland who want to find out about donating their bodies to medical science should contact the Senior Medical Officer, Department of Health, Social Services and Public Safety. (Contact details for these are on pages 274 and 271.)

## Chapter 15

# Death and dying

This chapter looks at the many difficult issues that may arise when someone is dying, or has recently died. Much of it looks at the roles of government departments and state bodies other than the NHS. For example, the role of coroners and of register offices (to register deaths).

## Diagnosis

A diagnosis of a life-threatening illness can be very shocking to receive. You may find you have not been able to take in everything you have been told by the doctor or consultant about the illness, and what may happen next. If you have any questions, you should talk to your GP or the consultant. Ask about any local support groups, and whether there is someone you can talk to in private about any aspect of the illness.

## Palliative care

Palliative care describes a particular approach to the care of people facing life-threatening illness. It aims to provide relief from pain, and to offer support to patients so they can have as active a life as possible until their death. It also supports the families of, and others close to, someone with such an illness. This includes support once the person has died.

There is nothing in the palliative care approach that aims either to speed up or to postpone death. Instead, it accepts that dying is a normal process and tries to support the patient as much as possible during this time.

Many people think that palliative care, which can be provided in hospices as well as in your own home, is only for people who are terminally ill with cancer. Whilst it is true that many services have been aimed at people with cancer, there is a much greater understanding now of the range of life-threatening illnesses and of the need for end-of-life care for everyone.

In the summer of 2004, the Government announced plans to increase the funding given to Strategic Health Authorities (StHAs) for end-of-life care. This is mostly being used to train existing health and social care professionals in end-of-life care approaches and techniques. One of the main aims is to support patients so that they can live and die in the place of their choice. For older people, for example, this means reducing the numbers who are transferred from their care home to an NHS hospital in the last week of their life if they would rather remain in the care home. Because of this, the extra training will not be just for NHS hospital staff but will also be for some of the staff working in care homes run by private individuals and companies and by charities as well as for GPs. There are also plans to make sure that, where there are Specialist Palliative Teams in the NHS, the patients referred are not just those with cancer.

There is more about palliative care, and about continuing NHS health care for people who it is thought are likely to die soon, in Chapter 13. If you, or someone you know, have been told that you have a life-threatening illness, start by asking your GP about what help and support is available locally.

# Hospices and other services

Hospices were first set up as charities, and most are still run by voluntary organisations. They may receive some NHS funding but often rely on donations from members of the public.

Although most people think of hospice care as somewhere you go and stay, some hospices also provide support to you at home, or offer other daytime support. Two charities, Help the Hospices and St Christopher's Hospice, have joined forces to provide Hospice Information, which can tell you about hospice services in your area and about other palliative care services (their addresses are on page 276).

Other services include specialist nursing services, including Macmillan and Marie Curie nurses (addresses on page 278), and are named after the two cancer charities. These specially trained nurses are often part of NHS specialist palliative care teams.

# End-of-life issues

This section of the chapter looks at some of the more controversial issues about the end of someone's life. You may find some of these sections upsetting, especially if someone close to you has recently died. But the reason for including the information is to explain what might happen in these very difficult situations.

## Do-not-resuscitate (DNR) decisions

Resuscitation means cardiopulmonary resuscitation (CPR), carried out when a patient's cardiac (heart) or respiratory (breathing) function stops. The Department of Health has issued guidance to the NHS setting out the four circumstances when a 'Do Not Resuscitate' (DNR) decision can be made:

- If a patient's condition is such that resuscitation is unlikely to succeed.
- If a patient who has the capacity to understand and make this decision has consistently stated or recorded the fact that he or she does not want to be resuscitated.
- If there is an advance directive or a Living Will that the patient has drawn up, stating he or she does not want to be resuscitated.
- If successful resuscitation would not be in the patient's best interests because it would lead to an intolerable quality of life.

Each NHS hospital consultant is responsible for the resuscitation policy used. The responsibility for the decision not to resuscitate a patient also lies with the consultant in charge of that patient's care.

This does not mean that the consultant makes the decision on his or her own. It should be discussed with other members of the medical and nursing team. Although this is a very sensitive issue, doctors should also talk about DNR issues and decisions with patients whenever possible, as well as with their families (but see Chapter 17 about sharing medical information with people other than the patient). This may be especially helpful with decisions affecting quality of life. The doctor in charge of the patient's care should record in their medical notes any decision taken; this should also be copied by nursing staff into nurses' notes.

There is more about advance directives and Living Wills in Chapter 8.

If you (or someone close to you) feel that doctors are making the wrong judgement about your quality of life because of your serious illnesses and disabilities, and this is adversely affecting their views about DNR in your case, the Disability Rights Commission (page 272) may be able to advise.

# Euthanasia and assisted suicide

Many people find the idea of euthanasia and assisted suicide completely unacceptable. Others firmly believe that these are the better options given the inevitable, and often terrible, circumstances they are facing. *This book does not tell you what beliefs you should hold about life and death nor how you should behave in this respect. It is, rightfully, a matter entirely for you. However, it is important that you know that both euthanasia and assisted suicide are illegal in the UK.*

The difference between the two relates to who causes the death. In *euthanasia*, someone else causes the death of the person (for example, by injecting a drug); in *assisted suicide*, it is the person who causes his or her own death but is helped to do this (for example, the person injects him- or herself – but someone else gets the drug for them). In both, you are able to understand that you are asking for help to end your own life.

There is some important case law about this issue, particularly the case of Diane Pretty. Mrs Pretty had a degenerative neurological condition. This meant that she was gradually losing control over her body: losing the ability to walk or to use her arms or to speak. Eventually the condition can lead to being unable to swallow. If other internal organ failure followed, the lungs would fill with fluid, leading to death. There is currently no cure for the condition: the question was when, not if, Mrs Pretty might die.

If things became too intolerable for her but Mrs Pretty wasn't physically able to take her own life, she wanted to know that if her husband helped her to die he would not face a prison sentence. However, the UK's law would not allow for this and her case was not successful.

There have been some other high-profile cases where people have chosen to end their lives in overseas clinics set up for this purpose.

But where someone else has helped them make the arrangements, and perhaps gone with them, in some cases this person has been investigated by the police on their return to the UK.

Some people have been trying to say that the proposed Mental Capacity Bill will allow euthanasia 'by the back door'. This is despite the Bill having a clause specifically saying that nothing in the Bill changes the UK's law – euthanasia will still be illegal. These concerns are more about people refusing medical treatment and about the circumstances when treatment might be withdrawn or withheld. Whether or not this Bill becomes law, people may still refuse treatment and doctors may still withdraw or withhold treatment. (See Chapter 8 for more about the Mental Capacity Bill.)

## Withholding or withdrawing treatment

The first important point is that you can always refuse treatment. Provided that you have the mental capacity to make this decision for yourself, you are perfectly within your rights to decide not to have a particular treatment even though you know that, as a result, you might die sooner than if you had the treatment (see Chapter 8 for more information about mental capacity). If you refuse a treatment, and this goes against what your doctor or other clinician believes to be the right thing to do, they may arrange for another doctor who does not find your decision difficult to follow to be responsible for your care.

You are equally entitled to ask doctors to do everything they can for you. This does not mean, however, that you have the right to receive all the services you ask for from the NHS. It's important not to confuse the two. Asking doctors to do everything they can means in part what is possible for them to do, and this may vary according to your current health circumstances.

For example, to perform a particular procedure you may need to have a usable artery, and you may no longer have one. It will also vary according to what the NHS provides over all. There may be an operation that is available in only one hospital in the USA: the fact that the operation exists doesn't mean the NHS will pay for you to travel to the USA to have the treatment. You will probably have read lots of stories in your local newspaper, or heard appeals on local radio, from people trying to raise funds to fly someone – often a child – for an operation overseas (usually the USA) that is not available in this country or on the NHS.

Both rights are very important. It is also important that you understand it is your right to choose between the two. You might be happy to accept some treatments but want to refuse others. The treatments you could refuse or ask for range from having a tooth extracted to treatment that will prolong your life.

The biggest difficulties arise when the treatment you want, or are refusing, might prolong your life.

## Life-prolonging treatments

The withholding or withdrawing of life-prolonging treatments is a very difficult issue for everyone concerned, including doctors. They have to follow guidance from the General Medical Council (GMC). In the summer of 2004, some aspects of this guidance were successfully challenged in the law courts. Since then, the GMC has been looking again at these specific areas where the guidance should be rewritten so that it fits entirely with UK law.

The challenge was brought by Mr Burke, who has a degenerative brain condition. It was about whether the guidance was in line with the European Convention on Human Rights, which is now part of UK law in the form of the Human Rights Act 1998. It looked at who could make decisions about artificial hydration and nutrition (Box 20).

---

### Box 20. Artificial hydration and nutrition

Sometimes people are not able to take in any nutrition or hydration (food or liquid) by mouth for some reason, such as being in a coma. Instead, help is provided artificially, for example by putting a feeding tube into the person's stomach.

The case involving the Hillsborough survivor Tony Bland decided that artificial nutrition and hydration is a medical procedure.

---

Mr Burke wanted to make sure that, in the event that he wasn't able to make his own decision at the time, his wishes that he should always be provided with artificial hydration and nutrition would be respected. The judgement confirmed that doctors are not obliged to provide treatment that is futile – that is, treatment that will make no difference to the patient. Doctors do not have to provide treatment that would place an 'intolerable burden' on the patient.

The 2004 judgement also said that patients who can make their own decisions should be able to decide whether or not they think artificial nutrition and hydration is in their best interests, and have this view respected.

If they are in a coma and cannot make this decision but they have made a statement in advance that they want to be provided with artificial nutrition and hydration, doctors must follow this. Again, this comes down to your right to make your own decision and to have that decision respected and acted on – no matter what it is. If a doctor disagrees, he or she must pass the care of the patient to another doctor who will provide the artificial nutrition and hydration. There is more about advance decisions and advance statements in Chapter 8.

Some people have been seriously worried about this issue because of their disabilities or illnesses. They are very concerned that they, not doctors, should decide about whether the quality of life they have is 'good enough' to mean that everything is done to help them remain alive. The Disability Rights Commission (see page 272) may be able to advise if this affects you or someone you know.

If there are disagreements – for example, the doctor treating a patient and the patient's family disagree about what should happen next – these should be taken to the courts to decide. While a court ruling is being sought, life-prolonging treatment can be provided.

Making your own decisions and having these followed doesn't always mean prolonging your life. In the case involving Miss B, she was able to express her views and could understand the decisions she was making. Following a major accident, she decided she wanted treatment and support machinery to be removed, knowing that this would lead to her death. The courts agreed she was able to make that decision for herself and her wishes were respected. The doctors and nurses who had been caring for her, however, asked not to be involved in this final stage. This request was respected and another team of staff was involved.

*Much of the case law referred to here is about very particular individual circumstances. They help us to understand what the law means in those circumstances, but new situations will always need to be looked at as and when they arise.*

Sometimes, there really is nothing more that can be done for someone. The person might be on a life-support machine and only this is keeping their internal organs working. Hospital staff may ask you, as their next of kin, to decide when to turn off the machine. You may well want to talk to someone for support before and after the decision. Ask NHS hospital staff whom you can talk to there. (See also page 210.)

# When someone dies
## Certifying and registering a death

When someone dies, the first official item that will be needed is a medical certificate that states the cause of the person's death. You will need to take this certificate with you when you go to the local register office. Deaths in England or Wales must be registered within five days. The register office is usually called 'Births, Marriages and Deaths'. The offices are generally in council buildings such as the Town Hall (in county areas, the register office is usually in the County Council's main office or county hall). You should ideally register the death in the district where the person has died but you can register their death in an office elsewhere. If you do register it elsewhere, it may take a day or two longer for all the paperwork to be completed.

You will probably need to make an appointment at the register office to register the death; your local office will be able to tell you when they are open, if an appointment is needed and how long it will take. They should also explain what documents you need to bring with you. When you are there, they will fill in all the forms needed and issue you with the death certificate, showing the details of the person who has died. You will need this in order to arrange the burial or cremation. Although you will be given one copy of the death certificate, you can buy additional copies from the registrar. It is worth doing this at the time, as you will need extra copies in order to do things such as close bank accounts and notify insurance companies.

If the person died in hospital or in their own home (including in a care home in which they have been living), their death can be registered by any one of:

- a relative;
- someone present when they died;
- someone else who lives in the person's house, or a member of staff from the hospital if this is where the person died;
- the person making the arrangements with the funeral director.

If someone dies elsewhere (ie not at home or in hospital), the person who found the body can also register the death.

The registrar will also issue a certificate for the burial or cremation of the body. This is usually passed to the funeral director, who cannot go ahead with funeral arrangements without it.

There will also be a certificate to be filled in and sent to the local Pensions Service office. This tells the Department for Work and Pensions that the person has died, because their state retirement pension and other state benefits stop being paid once they have died.

Sometimes, registrars will report a death to the coroner. They must do this if:

- there is no doctor who can issue a medical certificate stating the cause of death;
- the person had never been seen by the doctor who is issuing the medical certificate giving cause of death; or had been seen by that doctor in the past but not in the last 14 days of their life;
- the cause of death is unknown;
- the cause of death is believed to be unnatural or suspicious;
- the death happened during an operation or before the person had recovered from an anaesthetic;
- the death is due to industrial disease or industrial poisoning.

The death certificate cannot be issued, and the funeral arrangements cannot go ahead, while the coroner is looking into the matter.

The Coroner's Section of the Home Office has a leaflet, *When Sudden Death Occurs*, which is available in several languages and formats and may be helpful (contact details on page 276).

## Coroner's inquests and post-mortems

It is up to the coroner to decide whether to investigate the deaths referred to them. The coroner can decide whether a post-mortem is needed: this involves examining the body, including looking at internal organs, to see if the cause of death can be established.

Once the coroner has decided not to investigate, or has completed the investigations, they will tell the registrar. The registrar can then register the death and issue the relevant certificates.

If the coroner needs to investigate, this may cause some delays to funeral arrangements. In some religious beliefs, it is very important that the person be buried or cremated as soon as possible after they have died. If the person who has died held these beliefs, make sure you let the coroner's office know about this and ask them to do everything possible to speed up the process.

Some people may object strongly to a post-mortem being carried out, whether for religious, cultural or personal reasons. If you feel this way, you can put your objections in writing to the coroner. If the coroner still believes that a post-mortem is essential, you can appeal to the Divisional Court. Be aware that doing this will, inevitably, mean a further delay.

The results of any post-mortem should be shared as soon as possible with the relatives of the person who has died. The person's GP and/or consultant will also be told the results. The coroner's office may also decide to inform the police, if there are suspicions of foul play; but the coroner should tell you what, if anything, is going to happen next.

---

**Box 21. Retaining organs**

Serious concerns were raised that internal organs and other human tissues were kept (retained) by the NHS after the post-mortem of babies and young children at Alder Hey Hospital (the Royal Liverpool Children's Hospital) but without the knowledge or permission of their parents or legal guardians. This led to an inquiry, which made a number of recommendations.

Consent must be obtained to use human tissues after the person has died. Once the coroner's enquiries have been completed, the organs and tissues taken during a post-mortem must be returned to the body, unless relatives have given specific permission for these to be kept and used in research, for example.

The Human Tissues Act 2004 sets out many of these requirements.

---

When the results of a post-mortem are known, the coroner may decide to hold an inquest into what led to the person's death. This is not the same thing as a criminal trial. The coroner's office will explain what might be involved if an inquest is to be held.

Sometimes the NHS hospital in which the person died will ask for a post-mortem to be carried out, to help them understand more about a particular disease or condition. But they have to get permission from the patient's relatives to do so.

# Dealing with the body

Every NHS hospital should have a procedure for handling the death of patients. This can include written instructions for staff, reminding them of the importance of finding out the wishes of the dying patient, relatives and close friends on matters such as whether they want to be present during the time leading up to death, about being told about the death, and about any religious and cultural practices.

Some religious beliefs require the mouth and eyes of someone who has died to be closed, or for their feet to face a door, or for their heads to be covered.

You have the right to expect that NHS staff will respect the religious and cultural beliefs of the person who has died. You may need to tell staff what this involves. If you are unhappy about any aspect of the person's death, you can complain using the NHS complaints process (see Chapter 16). Although people are often understandably distressed when someone dies, and making a complaint may be the last thing you want to have to think about, if the behaviour or attitude of either particular staff or the hospital as a whole changes for the better, you will be helping other families in the future. Do bear in mind, though, that even if you are extremely upset because of how the person's body or their death has been handled, violence and abusive behaviour towards NHS staff will not be tolerated.

The person's body can be moved within England and Wales for burial or cremation purposes. If the body is in England or Wales and you want it moved to somewhere in Scotland, Northern Ireland, the Isle of Man, the Channel Islands or overseas, you will need the permission of the coroner's office in the area where the body is now. You will be asked to complete Form 104 (available from either the coroner or the registrar) and to give this to the coroner together with any certificate for burial or cremation that has already been issued. The coroner will then tell you when the body can be moved. This is usually four complete days after your application was received. If you want the body moved abroad, you need to ask the airline or other transport company what requirements they have (for example, airlines require that the body be embalmed).

You should note that, if the person has died in hospital but you want their body to be moved to another part of the country, the NHS does not have to pay the costs of transport. You will probably have to pay for this yourself.

## Funeral arrangements

If someone dies in hospital and relatives cannot be traced, or relatives cannot afford to pay for a funeral and do not qualify for a funeral payment from the Social Fund, the hospital has a duty to arrange and pay for burial or cremation. The hospital should try to find out whether the patient had any views on whether they wanted to be buried or cremated. This might involve asking staff, if the patient had been in hospital for a long time, as well as asking any relatives or friends. The hospital should also try to find out whether the patient held any particular religious views. If so, a minister from that religion should be present to conduct the ceremony. If it is not possible to find out the patient's beliefs or views, the hospital should arrange for cremation.

If the hospital believes that relatives could afford to arrange and pay for the funeral themselves although the relatives say otherwise, the hospital can ask the local authority in whose area the body lies to arrange for burial or cremation. This comes under the Public Health (Control of Disease) Act 1984. Note, though, that if you make the arrangements and pay for a funeral the local authority cannot reimburse you.

If a care home resident dies and there is no one who can pay for the funeral, this will be organised by the relevant social services department.

When the NHS or social services pays for funerals, these tend to be fairly basic affairs. They often have an agreement with a local firm of funeral directors who will carry this out on their behalf.

There is more about the Social Fund and other aspects of funeral arrangements in Age Concern Factsheet 27 *Planning for a funeral.*

## Dealing with bereavement

One of the many recommendations of the Alder Hey inquiry (see Box 21) was to remind the NHS that it has to provide bereavement counselling to the families and friends of patients who have died, as well as to staff. This is usually offered immediately after the person has died. But it is up to you whether to take up the offer of counselling, which typically involves you talking to a trained bereavement counsellor about what has happened and about your feelings. The counsellor may offer suggestions on what you could do next, whom else to talk to, and other advice.

Some people who would rather not talk to someone straight away decide that they would like to see someone later on. Ask your GP if this is something they can help organise for you, or for other suggestions. Many people who have been bereaved find it helpful to talk at least once to someone who has an understanding of how they may be feeling. (See also page 106.)

You may also want to talk to someone at a voluntary organisation such as Cruse Bereavement Care. It offers counselling and advice throughout the UK (contact details on page 270).

Age Concern Factsheet 27 *Planning for a funeral* has details of other voluntary organisations that may be helpful.

# Other issues

## Death-bed marriages

Someone who wants to marry and is not expected to recover but who is too ill to be moved to a place registered for marriage ceremonies can get a special licence to marry where they are. Their fiancé (or fiancée) would have to arrange this with the superintendent registrar at the register office that covers the part of the country where they will get married.

The registrar will need a certificate from a medical practitioner (such as the person's GP or the hospital consultant) to confirm that the person cannot be married in a licensed venue because they are too ill to move and will not recover.

It is also possible to arrange a Church of England marriage for the reasons above. In this case, the best thing to do is speak to the hospital chaplain or the vicar or rector of the parish where you live.

## Equipment, property and possessions

If the person who has died has been using equipment provided by the NHS or social services departments (perhaps by the Joint Equipment Store run by both), you should contact them as soon as you can to let them know the person has died. They may want to collect the equipment but they will tell you what needs to be arranged.

You might also want to speak to the person's GP about cancelling any NHS appointments that are pending. There may be lots of people you need to let know, such as the person's dentist and optometrist. You don't have to tell these professionals – but if you don't, reminders about check-ups and other appointments might still arrive addressed to the person who has died and you could find this very upsetting.

The safekeeping of the possessions of someone who has died in an NHS hospital is not the responsibility of the hospital. They should, however, hand these over to anyone responsible for administering the person's estate (usually called an Executor and named in the person's Will).

There is more about this in Age Concern Factsheet 14 *Dealing with someone's estate.*

If the person was living in a care home when they died, you should check what their contract with the home says. Some care homes charge for the room for a certain period of time after the person has died – for example, for 28 days. During this time, you should be able to collect the person's belongings from the room. But the home will expect the room to have been cleared by the end of the time specified in the contract.

Further information about contracts with care homes is in Age Concern Factsheet 29 *Finding care home accommodation.*

# Chapter 16

# Making complaints

This chapter explains the ways you can make a complaint about different issues. It highlights support to which you are entitled in making your complaint, explores how the NHS considers cases of negligence and compensation, and explains the role of the National Patient Safety Agency. It is also looks briefly at complaints about health care bought privately.

## Complaining about the NHS

Some things cannot be dealt with under the NHS complaints procedure; for example:

- Complaints about health care treatment you have paid for privately (see page 244).
- Events about which you are already taking legal action (although if you are taking legal action about one issue and there are other matters you want to raise, you can use the NHS complaints process for these other matters).

The NHS complaints system cannot look at complaints that are really about your local authority social services department. Some complaints 'straddle' both NHS and social services issues, however. For example, if someone is being discharged from an NHS hospital and they think this was done badly, and there were also problems because the care that social services was going to provide for them on their return home wasn't ready, they might need to complain to both organisations – even though the complaint is about the same 'event'. In these cases, the NHS has been told it must co-operate fully with any complaint raised with social services.

---

Age Concern Factsheet 41 *Local authority assessment for community care services* explains the social services complaints system.

---

As well as using the NHS complaints procedure described below, you can also complain about an individual NHS professional to their registering body (discussed later, under 'Making complaints about individual professionals'). You can also raise concerns about treatment with the National Patient Safety Agency (see page 11).

The NHS complaints procedure, which changed on 30 July 2004, is set out in Parliamentary Regulations. There will be some additional changes during 2005. The procedure applies to any NHS service in England. It also applies to Special Health Authorities that work across the UK – for example, the National Blood Service.

## Who can complain?

You have the right to complain about the treatment and care (or its lack) that you have received. Your complaint might be about any number of things. For example, you may believe you have been discriminated against because of your age; or your complaint might be about lack of privacy or of single-sex wards; about the poor behaviour of staff; or about inappropriate care. You can also complain about decisions your local Primary Care Trust makes about commissioning (funding) or planning NHS services. Chapter 18 looks at other ways you can be involved in influencing local and national NHS decisions. If a mistake was made in your care, you may have grounds for seeking financial compensation for any injuries that resulted, for example (see page 242).

Sometimes people are worried about making complaints. They are anxious that it might get them (or staff) into trouble – for example, if it is about a particular NHS professional or service that they know they will still need to call on after the complaint has been dealt with. But, unless complaints are made, NHS staff and organisations may not know whether mistakes are being made or inadequate care provided. They need to be told about this so that they can take steps to improve health care experiences for other NHS patients. Many of the charities that offer advice and information will be able to give you details of the various complaints systems and what to do. For example, Elderly Accommodation Counsel (contact details on page 273) has an information sheet that will help guide you as you go about making a complaint.

You also have the right to complain about the care someone else received if he or she:

■ has died;
■ is a child (and you are the child's parent or legal guardian);
■ cannot make the request him- or herself because of physical or mental incapacity;
■ has asked you to act on his or her behalf.

If you are acting on someone else's behalf, the person responsible for dealing with NHS complaints will need to be sure that the person has given their consent. So you should not be surprised if you are asked to produce a letter or some other proof from the person saying you have their permission. Even if this upsets you, think how much more upsetting it would be if someone claimed to represent you without your agreement.

If you are acting for someone who has died or who lacks the capacity to bring their own complaint, the NHS complaints manager is within their rights to expect that you are either a relative or you have (or had) sufficient interest in their welfare to take on this role now – for example, you were the person's spouse or partner. (See also Chapter 8.)

If the complaints manager does not accept that you are a suitable person to take this forward, they must write to you and explain why. (You could challenge this decision but you would need to set out the reasons why you are suitable.) One reason the complaints manager might give is that the patient has previously said they do not wish their health information be discussed with a third party (see Chapter 17): you would count as a third party because you are neither the patient (the first party) nor the NHS body (the second party). If your main aim is simply to make sure the complaint is looked at, you could then ask how the complaint will be taken forward if you are not involved. There is no absolute right for you to be able to pursue a complaint on behalf of anybody and everybody, but it would be unusual for a complaint not to be considered at all just because of your lack of suitability.

You can complain verbally (in person or on the telephone), in writing or by email. Make sure that your complaint reaches the right person. There are time limits within which the NHS must consider your complaint, so it will be recorded as starting on the date the complaint was received. In the case of written complaints, this would be when the letter reached the relevant organisation.

There are also time limits that apply to you. You must make your complaint:

■ within six months of the event; *or*

■ within six months of your realising there was something to complain about, as long as it is not more than twelve months after the event itself took place.

These time limits can be waived if there are good reasons why you could not complain sooner. You will be probably be asked to explain what these reasons are.

The first stage of making (and dealing with) a complaint is sometimes called 'local resolution'. There are slightly different arrangements, depending on whether your complaint is about a primary care provider (such as your GP or an optometrist), about a Primary Care Trust or NHS Trust, or about an NHS Foundation Trust. These are all described below.

Do remember that if your complaint is about treatment that you have paid for privately, these NHS arrangements will not apply.

## Complaints about a Primary Care Trust or NHS Trust

Each Primary Care Trust and NHS Trust must appoint someone to act as a complaints manager. The person with this role may have a different job title but it should be obvious that they handle complaints. The complaints manager deals with complaints made by members of the public as well as by NHS staff.

Trusts must also make sure that a senior person in the organisation (for example, a member of the Board of Directors) has overall responsibility for making sure that each Trust meets the requirements of the complaints system. Each Trust must also have a Patient Advice and Liaison Service to help support patients in raising issues and complaints (Box 22).

**Box 22. The Patient Advice and Liaison Service and the Independent Complaints Advocacy Service**

Every Primary Care Trust and NHS Trust must have a Patient Advice and Liaison Service (PALS). Your local PALS will be able to explain what making a complaint involves, but it will probably start by seeing if it can help to sort out any issues or concerns you have. It can also provide information on local services and support groups. This includes details of your local Independent Complaints Advocacy Service (ICAS).

There is an ICAS covering every Primary Care Trust area. They provide advocacy services for people making formal complaints about NHS services.

You can find contact details for your local PALS and ICAS services by:

■ contacting NHS Direct;

■ contacting your local Primary Care Trust;

■ looking in the telephone directory.

You should receive an acknowledgement of your complaint within two days of its being received. This will probably be a short letter saying that your complaint has been received and is being looked into. You may also be sent details of the complaints procedure, including the role of the Healthcare Commission. It should also be explained to you that, in investigating your complaint, it may be necessary to share information about you. This should involve only information relevant to your complaint (for example, details of your operation and why this was needed), and should be shared only with the people the Trust needs to speak to for the investigation. (See also Chapter 17.)

At this stage, you should also be told about your right to assistance from the Independent Complaints Advocacy Service (Box 22).

When looking into your complaint, the NHS complaints manager can decide to arrange mediation or conciliation services in order to try to resolve the complaint. This would involve your meeting with someone working as a mediator (probably from an organisation specialising in this kind of support), who is not involved in this complaint in any way. The mediator would also work with those you are complaining about. Both you and the others involved in the complaint have to agree to take part in mediation, however.

You can also request a mediator. Trusts must offer this service. Mediation can be a good way of resolving disputes – for example, ones that are based on misunderstandings on both sides. Sometimes people feel this is a 'soft option' and want to continue with the formal complaints route but it can be an effective way of helping staff understand how they come across to patients, and changing their behaviour as a result. But it is up to you whether you want to try this. If the mediation is unsuccessful, you can tell the complaints manager that you want to continue with the formal complaint.

You should be told the outcome of your complaint within 20 working days of your complaint being made (or 10 working days if your complaint is about any aspect of a GP practice). A 'working day' is Monday through Friday (ie weekdays). This means you have to ignore weekends and Bank Holidays when working out the date by when you should hear the outcome.

Sometimes it can take the complaints manager longer than 20 working days to reach their conclusion (or 10 days in the case of complaints about a GP practice). This might be because it is a very complicated issue or because a key member of staff they need to talk to is away. In this case, they must reply as quickly as possible after the 20 days. In the meantime they must write to you and explain why there is a delay. The complaints manager should contact you to discuss this delay so that you can both agree the new date by which you will hear.

When you receive the response to your complaint, you should also be given information about taking the complaint to the next stage, if you want to. The next stage is to ask for an independent review by the Healthcare Commission. You can do this if you are not satisfied with how the complaint has been handled or you are unhappy about the outcome (see page 231).

One of the outcomes from this stage may be an apology for what has happened. It is important that you know that the NHS has been told that an apology is not an admission of liability. In the past, people have often asked for an apology but did not receive one because it was believed that saying sorry meant the NHS was accepting it was at fault in legal terms. This issue had become very mixed up with concerns about legal claims for negligence and compensation (see page 242). It is perfectly possible to be sorry that someone has had an experience that was terrible for them without this automatically meaning the NHS was legally responsible.

## Complaints to NHS Foundation Trusts

One of the 'freedoms' that NHS Foundation Trusts have is that they can draw up and use their own complaints procedure. However, if they do not have a procedure and you have a complaint about a Foundation Trust, or if you use their procedure and are unhappy with the outcome, you can take your complaint to the Healthcare Commission.

The Healthcare Commission can only consider complaints about NHS Foundation Trusts if they are made by patients and are about the provision by the Trust of health care or other services to patients (or care delivered on behalf of the Trust). If your complaint is about something else, or you are not the patient, the Healthcare Commission must refer your complaint to the Independent Regulator (Box 23). Even if the complaint is something the Healthcare Commission can investigate, and provided it has your agreement, it will in any case seek the views of the Independent Regulator. It will share your complaint with the Independent Regulator in order to do so.

Unless you clearly say otherwise, the Healthcare Commission will assume it has your permission to share your complaint with the Independent Regulator.

---

**Box 23. The Independent Regulator**

The Independent Regulator is the formal title of the organisation responsible for authorising, monitoring and regulating NHS Foundation Trusts. Its everyday name (or working name) is Monitor. It is independent from the Department of Health but its members are appointed by the Secretary of State for Health.

Contact details of Monitor (the Independent Regulator for NHS Foundation Trusts) are on page 279.

---

## The Healthcare Commission

Since 30 July 2004, the Healthcare Commission has had the responsibility of carrying out independent reviews of complaints. This used to be the responsibility of the Chief Executive of the NHS Trust about whom you were complaining but has changed because of concerns that this arrangement might not be as independent as was needed.

You must contact the Healthcare Commission within two months of your receiving the outcome of your original complaint. You will need to complete a Healthcare Commission complaints form. Your local Primary Care Trust or Independent Complaints Advocacy Service should have copies they can give you; or you can contact the Healthcare Commission and ask for one to be posted to you; or you can download and print a copy from its website (see page 275 for contact details).

If you don't want to complete the form, you can write to the Healthcare Commission with your request, but do make sure you send the copy of the report (the response, or outcome) that you were sent at the end of the local complaints stage, as discussed above. This first stage is sometimes called 'local resolution'.

The Healthcare Commission can also look at some complaints about health care services you have bought privately. This is because it also regulates private and voluntary sector health care providers (see page 10).

There are some circumstances in which the Healthcare Commission cannot carry out independent reviews:

- You have stated in writing that you are taking legal proceedings.
- The NHS Foundation Trust concerned is taking (or is proposing to take) disciplinary action against their member of staff who is the subject of your complaint.
- The complaint arises out of an NHS Foundation Trust's (alleged) failure to comply with a request for data under the Data Protection Act 1998 or a request for information under the Freedom of Information Act 2000.
- The complaint is being or has been investigated by the Health Service Commissioner (the Health Ombudsman – see page 234).

Once it has received your complaint, and provided this is something it can review, the Healthcare Commission must tell you what it has decided to do next as soon as is 'reasonably practicable' – hopefully within 10 working days. Its decision may be:

- not to take any further action; *or*
- to recommend the action that the organisation concerned should take; *or*
- to investigate the complaint further; *or*
- to consider the subject of the complaint as part of any other investigation or review that it is carrying out (or proposing to carry out) as part of its overall role (see page 10), *or*
- to refer the complaint to the relevant professional body (see page 236); *or*
- to refer the complaint to the Health Service Ombudsman.

Whatever the decision, the Healthcare Commission must give reasons. It must also send a copy of its decision to the person or the organisations that you are complaining about. It can choose to send the decision to any other organisation that the Healthcare Commission believes has an interest in the matter. If it is to investigate further, you should ask how quickly it expects to be able to complete this and let you know its findings.

If the Healthcare Commission recommends action to the local organisation involved, and you are still dissatisfied, you can ask the Healthcare Commission to look at the complaint again.

If an investigation is needed, you have the right to request a panel of three members of the public to hear your complaint. The panel will hear evidence from you, the organisation you are complaining against, any witnesses involved and the Healthcare Commission's report. The panel will make recommendations about how to resolve your case and, when necessary, suggest service improvements.

If you are unhappy with the Healthcare Commission's decision, or if it investigates and you do not agree with the findings, you can take the matter to the Health Service Ombudsman.

## The Health Service Ombudsman

The Health Service Ombudsman investigates complaints made by or on behalf of someone who has suffered because of unsatisfactory treatment or service from the NHS. This could include the NHS not providing a service or a failure in service or maladministration. The Ombudsman also looks into complaints against private health providers, provided that the NHS funded the treatment. She can also investigate complaints about other services provided on behalf of the NHS, and can look at complaints about continuing NHS health care – including review panel decisions (see page 189). Contact details are on page 274.

Her office publishes a range of leaflets (in several languages and formats) explaining what she (and her staff, on her behalf) can and cannot investigate. They also explain how to make the complaint. You do not need to use a lawyer to bring a complaint to the Ombudsman but the usual expectation is that you have already taken the matter through local resolution and independent review stages. If you have not done this, and the Ombudsman thinks you should do so first, her office will write to you to let you know what steps you should take.

Unlike other parts of the complaints process, the Ombudsman does not accept complaints made by email. You will need to put your complaint in writing, and you may be asked to provide other documents to help back up your concerns.

It is up to the Ombudsman whether to investigate. If your complaint is not to be investigated, you will be sent a letter explaining why. If you disagree with this decision, and you have significant new (or fresh) evidence that was not available when you made your complaint, you can send this to the Ombudsman and ask for the decision not to investigate to be reconsidered. A member of staff who is more senior than the person who decided not to investigate will look at your new evidence and your original complaint. You should receive their decision within 18 days of your letter and new evidence reaching the Ombudsman's office.

If you don't have any significant new evidence but still disagree with the decision not to investigate, you can still write to the Ombudsman and explain why you think it should be looked into. You will receive a reply within 14 days, but this might still be a refusal to investigate. The Ombudsman does not have to investigate just because you have written.

If the Ombudsman decides to look into the matter on your behalf, you will receive a letter explaining what the next steps will be. Investigations can take a long time: the Ombudsman's office takes great pains to make sure it sees all the relevant material and may decide to interview all the people involved, including you. But the Ombudsman's office should keep you up to date about their progress.

Many (but not all) of the Ombudsman's investigations are published. You can either buy copies from The Stationery Office (page 283) or you can download copies from the Ombudsman's website (page 274). But everyone whose complaint is investigated receives a copy of this, even if the report is not published. Everyone mentioned in the report, including your relative or friend (if this matter is about someone else) has their details made anonymous (eg you might be referred to as 'Mrs W' when your name is actually Mrs Brown), so you will not be identified. In recent years, several of these investigations have highlighted matters of national concern regarding continuing NHS health care (see Chapter 13).

Although you can't appeal against the Ombudsman's decision, you can challenge it in the law courts through a judicial review. You would need legal advice on doing this, and advice on how you would pay for such legal action, as it can be very costly. Your local law centre or Citizens Advice Bureau may be able to point you in the right direction.

You can, however, complain further if you are concerned about *how* the Ombudsman dealt with your complaint. For example, under the Freedom of Information Act 2000 the Ombudsman has to give you reasons why some information might have been withheld from you. If you disagree with these reasons, you could raise the matter with the organisation that is responsible for the Freedom of Information issues – the Information Commissioner (see Chapter 17). But if you have other concerns about how your case was handled, you should write to the Ombudsman and let her know what these are.

The outcome of the Ombudsman's investigation can be to require the NHS to refund you for treatment you have had to buy privately, because, for example, the Ombudsman has ruled that it should have been funded by the NHS. It can also require the NHS organisation involved to make a payment to you in recognition that you have had to bring this action. But the Ombudsman cannot provide funds for compensation, nor insist that compensation for physical or mental injury (for example) is paid. These types of compensation claims are handled through a different route, as discussed later.

## Making complaints about individual professionals

The starting point is to tell someone – for example, a dental assistant, the GP, a receptionist – about your complaint. Often it can be sorted out there and then.

If you prefer, you can take a more formal route. You might want to do this if talking doesn't resolve the problem, or because you would rather not talk about this with the person who provides your care. All GPs, dentists, optometrists and pharmacies offering NHS services must have a complaints procedure and a senior member of staff who oversees this. The surgery or clinic concerned should be able to give you this information; if you are unsure, contact your local Primary Care Trust and ask whom you should complain to.

Once you have made a formal complaint, you should hear the outcome within 10 working days of its being received. A 'working day' is a weekday, so ignore Saturdays, Sundays and Bank Holidays when working out the date by which you should have the response.

If you are not happy with the decision or response, you can take your complaint to the Healthcare Commission (see page 231).

If the person you are complaining about works for the NHS, you can also make a complaint using the NHS's procedure. This is explained on page 226.

But if the person only works for themselves (eg they run a private dental clinic) you won't be able to use this NHS route.

Most health care professionals must be registered with a particular body relevant to their profession. For example, doctors must be registered with the General Medical Council. Sometimes this registration is called being licensed to practise.

If your concern is a case of serious misconduct, you may want to go straight to the body that registers that person and make your complaint. Serious misconduct includes fraud, abuse (whether physical, financial, emotional or sexual), unnecessary treatment or treatment resulting in injury. These are not the only examples.

If you believe a crime has been committed, you can also go to the police.

Many concerns are, however, not so serious as to need the involvement of the police or a formal complaint to the registering body. In such cases, in the first instance you should make your concerns known to the professional concerned. This can be hard to do, so you may want someone to help you do it. If you don't have a close friend or relative you would like to involve, you could ask your local Age Concern if they can help or if they can suggest someone you might approach.

Most clinics and individual professionals offer some arrangement for patients to make a complaint. Ask for details and then follow what is suggested. If you are still unhappy, or if you feel that how you are being asked to complain is a problem, approach the relevant registration body and raise your concerns with them.

## Complaints about doctors

All doctors must be registered to practise (sometimes known as 'being licensed to practise') with the General Medical Council (GMC). This applies to hospital doctors, GPs and those working in private clinics as well as for the NHS. It is illegal to work as a doctor unless you are registered.

If you have concerns about the actions or behaviour of a doctor, you can raise them with the General Medical Council. It has a guide for patients about how to make a complaint.

The General Medical Council can investigate and, if necessary, withdraw (strike off) or suspend the person's registration, which would make it unlawful for the person to work as a doctor in the UK. Examples of why someone might be 'struck off' include if they hit or otherwise abused a patient or stole from a patient. The role of the General Medical Council is beng reviewed by the Government during 2005 as part of a wider look at patient safety issues.

If a doctor commits a crime, you or the General Medical Council can also involve the police.

If the doctor you are complaining about works for the NHS, you can also make a complaint using the NHS's procedure.

## Complaints about nurses, health visitors or midwives

All nurses, health visitors and midwives must be registered with the Nursing and Midwifery Council (NMC).

The Nursing and Midwifery Council can investigate and, if necessary, withdraw (strike off) or suspend the person's registration. This would make it unlawful for that person to work as a nurse (or health visitor or midwife) in the UK. Examples of why someone might be 'struck off' include if they hit or otherwise abused a patient or stole from a patient.

If a nurse, health visitor or midwife commits a crime, you or the Nursing and Midwifery Council can also involve the police.

If the person you are complaining about works for the NHS, you can also make a complaint using the NHS's procedure.

## Complaints about dentists

All dentists, whether they offer NHS or private treatments, are registered by the General Dental Council (GDC). The General Dental Council also registers dental hygienists and dental therapists (sometimes these are collectively called dental auxiliaries).

The General Dental Council can remove a dental professional's registration, and without registration the person cannot lawfully work as a dentist. As with registration of doctors and nurses, removing an individual from the professional register is often reserved for the most serious of complaints. Different routes may be needed for other types of complaint. Anyone dissatisfied with the NHS dental treatment they have received can make a complaint using the NHS complaints procedure outlined earlier.

There have been concerns that the NHS cannot investigate complaints about private treatments. There have also been concerns that the General Dental Council can only discipline the dentists; it cannot offer anything such as an alternative approach that would sort out the problem from the patient's point of view. So some private patients have had to take individual legal action to achieve a remedy. Concern about these aspects has grown in recent years because of the reduction in NHS dentistry and the growth of private treatments.

Legislation is being introduced in 2005 to address this. Firstly, the General Dental Council will become a Special Health Authority. Secondly, it will then be able to investigate complaints about non-NHS dentistry. The Government has said that the necessary legislation should be in place in 2005 and the scheme should be launched as soon as possible after that. It will offer a telephone service, providing information to anyone with a dental complaint. People whose complaint relates to NHS dentistry will be referred, as now, to the appropriate NHS organisation. For complaints about non-NHS dentistry, the scheme aims to help patients and dental professionals resolve complaints swiftly and informally.

Whether your complaint is about NHS or private dentistry, however, most advice suggests that you should begin by making a complaint to the individual surgery or practice. Dentists offering NHS treatment will have a complaints procedure they work to; private practices may also have this (although they do not have to). If this approach is not successful, you can pursue your complaint through the routes described above.

## Complaints about optometrists

Dispensing opticians and optometrists are registered by the General Optical Council (GOC). As well as regulating individuals, the General Optical Council regulates organisations carrying on business as optometrists or dispensing opticians, for example the larger chains such as SpecSaver or Dollond & Aitchison.

## Complaints about therapists

Each of the therapies (eg occupational therapy, physiotherapy, arts therapy) has its own professional association or college: the College of Occupational Therapists, the Royal College of Speech and Language Therapists, the British Association of Arts Therapists, the British Association of Dramatherapists, the Association of Professional Music Therapists and the Chartered Society of Physiotherapy (contact details in the Appendix).

If you have a complaint about someone in one of these professions, you can contact the relevant association. If the individual is registered with the Health Professions Council (HPC), your complaint can also be made to that organisation. This can be done whether the person works for the NHS or runs their own private clinic. If there is anyone calling themselves an occupational therapist, a speech and language therapist, an art, drama or music therapist, or a physiotherapist, and is not registered with the Health Professions Council, tell the Council immediately so that it can take action. This could involve the person being prosecuted.

# Complaints about pharmacists/prescriptions

If your complaint is about a pharmacist, or about the owner of a pharmacy business, you can raise this with the Royal Pharmaceutical Society (contact details on page 282).

If your complaint is about an NHS prescription, you can also use the NHS complaints process as outlined earlier in this chapter.

If your complaint is about prescriptions by a doctor, nurse or dentist, you can complain about this to the professional organisation they have to register with. If they are providing services to you as an NHS patient, you can also follow the NHS complaints route.

# Complaints about chiropodists/podiatrists

If you think the chiropodist has behaved badly or the standard of care has not been good, you can contact the Health Professions Council. This applies both to private chiropodists and those who work in the NHS. If you are concerned about the NHS treatment you have received, you can also use the NHS complaints procedure.

## Claiming compensation from the NHS

The Government has set up and runs two specific compensation schemes for patients with particular illnesses. The first – the Skipton Fund, a UK-wide body – is for people who have contracted hepatitis C through NHS blood or blood-related products. Information is also available on the condition from the charity Hepatitis C Trust. (Contact details on pages 282 and 276.)

The second compensation scheme is for the small number of people who have so far developed variant Creutzfeldt–Jakob disease (vCJD). Compensation for people, and their families, with vCJD is administered by the vCJD Trust (contact details on page 284) – set up by the Secretary of State for Health to handle such claims. The charity the CJD Support Network (contact details on page 269) may also be helpful. To make a claim resulting from vCJD, you should contact either Rowena Hill or Edwina Rawson, at Charles Russell Solicitors (address on page 268).

Most other compensation claims arise out of issues of *clinical negligence*. This is where doctors and other clinicians have been remiss in their treatment of you. In other words, they have failed in their 'duty of care'. As a result you have sustained some form of injury, suffered pain or been disadvantaged in some other way. In the worst cases, someone might have died as a result of the negligent action. Negligence can include not taking action as well as doing something wrong such as giving someone the incorrect dose of medicine.

The NHS has a UK-wide compensation scheme for people who have been affected in this way. It is run by the NHS Litigation Authority (NHSLA). The NHS Litigation Authority is a Special Health Authority that covers the whole of the UK. Plans to change this system were announced in 2003 but as yet they have not been implemented.

During the autumn of 2004, the Legal Services Commission carried out a general consultation concerning the availability of Legal Aid for people pursuing clinical negligence cases. This aspect might affect your entitlement to help with the legal costs of such action. Your local law centre will be able to advise about this.

A good starting point, if you want to pursue this route, is to contact the charity Action for Victims of Medical Accidents (AvMA; address on page 264). AvMA has a team of legally trained caseworkers who can provide free and confidential advice after a medical accident. They can also suggest experienced solicitors, advise about legal challenges (such as seeking a judicial review, including how to pay for this), and give you a list of questions to ask if you want to find your own legal representative.

# Complaints about private health care services

Sometimes the NHS buys (or commissions) health care services from the private sector, on behalf of NHS patients. As far as patients are concerned, this still counts as NHS care because the NHS funds it even if a private organisation provides it. If your complaint is about the care the NHS has funded for you, you can use the NHS complaints procedure. You would need to complain to the NHS Trust that paid for the health care you received. Or you could choose to complain direct to the organisation that provided the service. Private health care providers must have a complaints procedure you can use, and they must give you details of this on request. Whichever way you complain, if you are not happy with the response you receive, you can ask the Healthcare Commission for an independent review.

If you have paid for your health care from a private health care organisation, you can make a complaint using its complaints procedure. You can also complain about individual professionals to the relevant organisation with which they must be registered – such as the General Medical Council or the Health Professions Council. (See also Chapters 3, 4, 5 and 7.)

Some NHS hospitals offer private 'pay beds'. Under this arrangement, you are treated as a private patient even though you may be on NHS premises. If you have a complaint about private pay bed treatment, you can use the NHS complaints procedure but only about issues to do with the facilities (such as the ward or room you were in, or the food) and non-medical staff (for example, the porters or the nursing staff – basically anyone who is not a doctor) provided by the NHS hospital in question. If you have a complaint about the medical input to your care from, say, the consultant, you have to complain about this to the General Medical Council (see page 238).

Even if the consultant also works for that NHS hospital as an NHS doctor, the NHS employer is not responsible for the consultant's private practice.

## Complaints about private doctors

If you are unhappy with a doctor's behaviour or treatment, you can complain to the General Medical Council. You may also be able to make a complaint to the Healthcare Commission, as some private clinics have to be regulated by them under the Care Standards Act 2000.

The NHS complaints procedure does not apply in the case of private treatment for which you have paid.

## **Other investigations**

The complaints and compensation systems outlined above are not the only way the NHS finds out about issues. Nor are they the only actions the NHS might take.

## Coroner's inquest and post-mortems

The coroner holds inquests into unexpected or suspicious deaths. The NHS is expected to liaise with the coroner's office, especially if such deaths might have involved NHS staff.

## Criminal offences

There is nothing to stop you, or the NHS, from calling the police if you believe that a criminal offence has taken place. This could include indecent assault, physical assault, harm or injury, or even death. The police should tell you whether this is something they can investigate.

## National Patient Safety Agency

The National Patient Safety Agency (NPSA) is a Special Health Authority that co-ordinates the system of reporting errors and 'incidents' (whether deliberate or accidental) across the country. It is believed that, if NHS staff are encouraged to report mistakes when they make them, lessons can be learned quickly and patient safety improved across the UK.

Both patients and carers can report any unexpected suffering or harm they have experienced as a result of contact with NHS services.

You should note, however, that you might still need to bring a complaint against the organisation involved, as outlined above. This is because the National Patient Safety Agency can't investigate individual complaints.

# Chapter 17

# Information and communication

There is a great deal of health care information you should be given.
You have a right to receive:

- Copies of letters that NHS doctors write to each other about your
  health (eg copies of letters about your care from your GP to a
  hospital consultant).
- A copy of your dental treatment plan (Chapter 4).
- A copy of any assessment of your health and care needs
  (Chapters 12 and 13) and a copy of any care plan, if services will
  be provided.

If you need this information in a particular form, such as large print,
Braille, recorded on a cassette tape or in a language other than
English, the NHS should provide this for you. Other information, such
as the decision whether or not to provide you with NHS fully funded
continuing health care (Chapter 13), may be recorded in your medical
notes (see page 250 for details of how to access these).

If the NHS care you need is provided only if you meet local criteria,
copies of these criteria should be available to you. If you are in
hospital, you should have information about how your discharge will
be handled; there may also be leaflets about what to expect while

you are in hospital. Your GP surgery should have leaflets explaining what it provides, when it is open and what to do if you are taken ill when it is closed.

Under the Freedom of Information Act 2000, since January 2005 public bodies (such as the Department of Health, local councils or the NHS) must say what information they publish, how the information is made available, and whether it is free or if there is a charge.

There may also be other information that you receive when you ask for treatment. For example, some hospital Accident and Emergency (A&E) units have a digital display showing approximate waiting times.

# If English is not your first language

One of the basic principles on which the NHS works is that everyone who is entitled to NHS care should have equal access to this.

If English is not your first language, or you have no spoken or written English at all, you may need some help with translations so that you can understand what is happening. Nurses, doctors and others also need to be able to talk to you.

All A&E units in England have copies of *The Emergency Multilingual Phrasebook*. This is funded by the Department of Health but produced by the British Red Cross. It covers, in 36 languages (from Albanian to Welsh), the most common medical questions and terms. Other organisations can buy copies from the British Red Cross (page 267), or it can be accessed on the Department of Health's website.

The aim of the *Phrasebook* is to help staff communicate with patients who do not speak English at this first, emergency, stage. It can also be helpful where the shock of accident or injury means that someone who, in ordinary circumstances would speak English, has reverted to their mother tongue. After using the *Phrasebook* to begin with, though, staff are likely to need to ask an interpreter to come into the hospital.

Some NHS Trusts employ their own interpreters; others use interpreters from other organisations. If no one who speaks a particular language can be found, the hospital or clinic may contact a telephone interpreter service such as Language Line.

If you need an interpreter, you will not be asked to pay for this. In non-emergency settings your language needs may be noted in your health records. People may take a relative or friend with them who can speak English to translate for them but this is not always ideal. Some people feel that certain medical matters are very private and they do not want their family or friends to know all the details. In these cases, ask the surgery or health care professional how they can help you to have a more private consultation or treatment.

# Information before making decisions

Before you make decisions about certain treatments, you will need information about the benefits and risks to you of either agreeing or refusing a treatment. You should be told about alternative treatments, drugs or approaches. Depending on your particular health problem, you may also want to know about side effects (for example, the side effects of chemotherapy) or about any longer term problems that could arise.

The information should be given to you in a format that you can understand. If this means it needs to be in another language, for example, this should be made available. If you have a disability and need information in another format because of this, the NHS must provide it for you under the Disability Discrimination Act 1995.

You can ask for a second opinion about your condition or any proposed treatment – although this does not have to be provided (see page 40). You might also want more information about your condition or its treatment from NHS Direct (see page 25) or from a self-help group or charity that specialises in particular health issues, such as the Alzheimer's Society or the National Osteoporosis Society.

## Access to your health records

Access to your health records comes under the Data Protection Act 1998. This applies to records held by the NHS as well as by private or voluntary health care providers. A health record means information about your physical or mental health (or about the condition of any identified living person) made by or on behalf of a health professional who is connected with your care. This includes your GP, a hospital physiotherapist or a district nurse, for example.

The Date Protection Act gives everyone the right to ask to see health information kept about them. This might be written records or information stored on a computer. It includes X-rays, photographs or printouts from monitoring equipment. You can ask to see records no matter how long ago they were compiled (but see page 252, about how long these are kept after someone dies). But your right is only to ask to see your records – there is no law that says that whoever holds the records must agree to your request. Nevertheless, the NHS's current policy is always to agree to your seeing your records unless whoever holds the records thinks that something in them might:

- cause serious harm to your physical or mental health or condition or that of any other person; or
- where giving you access would reveal information about (or provided by) someone else who has not agreed to this being shared.

In such a situation, the person holding the records could either:

■ keep back some information, but let you see the rest; *or*
■ keep back the whole record and refuse any access.

The record holder (such as your GP surgery or hospital records office) doesn't have to explain why it is withholding access but, if this happens, you can complain about it. Approach the record holder in the first instance. Because this area comes under the Data Protection Act, if there is a dispute you can also contact the Information Commissioner (address on page 277) whose role it is to oversee matters that come under that Act.

If you want to see your health records, put your request in writing and send it to the organisation or professional holding your records.

There is a charge for you to see your NHS health records. The most you can be asked to pay is £10 for manual (written) records, and £50 for computer records (or where there is a mix of computer and manual records). You will have to pay this before a copy of your records will be made available. The amount you are asked to pay will depend on the cost to the NHS of making a copy and posting it to you. The charge has to cover these costs; some records (such as X-rays) are particularly expensive to copy. But you should not be asked to pay more than these maximum sums.

Once the organisation that holds your records has received this amount, and satisfied itself you are who you say you are, it should provide the copy to you between 21 and 40 days later. The 21-day target is something the NHS should try to achieve but it is not a legal requirement; however, the 40 day limit is a requirement under the Data Protection Act 1998.

## Amending your records

If, when you receive the copy of your health records, you think some information is missing or incorrect, you should first contact the organisation or individual holding the records and ask for this to be put right. If this is unsuccessful, and these are NHS records, you can make a complaint using the NHS complaints procedure explained in Chapter 16. You can also complain to the Information Commissioner, because the records come under the Data Protection Act (see page 251).

## Applying to see the records of someone who has died

You can apply to see the health records of someone who has died. You have to do this in writing to the organisation holding the records, and provide enough information to make sure that the correct records can be identified. When someone dies, their records are sent either to the local Primary Care Trust (the primary care records) and held for ten years, or are held for at least eight years by the hospital (or in the hospital's archive) where the person was treated. You may be asked about your connection with the person and about your right to access their records.

If anything in the person's records shows that they did not want these shared, those wishes will be respected and you will not be allowed to see their records. The organisation holding the records can also decide not to share their records if to do so might cause serious harm to you or another person, or would mean that information about another person would be shared without their consent. Otherwise, you will need to pay a fee and wait to receive a copy as outlined above.

# Agreeing for others to see your records

There is a Code of Practice about confidentiality that the NHS must follow. This means that you have to agree (give your consent) to any part of your health records being shared even if this is with another health care professional involved in your care. Giving consent doesn't have to be particularly formal but you should be asked. For some people, health care professionals will also want to share details with social care staff. Again, you should be asked if this is all right with you. If you're not sure, ask the staff involved to explain why this needs to happen, how it will benefit you and what might happen if you don't agree.

But there are some circumstances where your consent is not needed. For example:

- Any organisation with statutory powers to investigate complaints (such as the Healthcare Commission or the Health Service Ombudsman) can gain access to patients' medical records if these are needed to pursue their investigation.

- The courts, including coroner's courts (and some tribunals and people appointed to hold inquiries) have legal powers to require that relevant information be disclosed; in this case, although the person's consent is not needed, they should be told that this is happening.

The key principle of the duty to keep information confidential is that information given should be shared only with the permission of the person who gave it. The Human Rights Act gives us all a right to a private life but there are some circumstances when NHS staff might well break this confidence. These are generally to do with the prevention, exposure or investigation of serious crimes such as:

- murder or manslaughter;
- rape;
- treason;
- kidnapping;
- the abuse of someone (child or adult);
- any other cases where individuals have suffered serious harm;
- serious harm to the security of the state or to public order;
- crime involving substantial financial gain or loss.

Sometimes Members of Parliament (MPs) are asked by patients to raise matters with the NHS organisation relating to their concerns. If the MP writes to the NHS about your situation, the NHS will take this to mean that you agree to details of what has happened in your care to be shared with the MP if this is needed in order to answer the points made in the MP's letter.

# If you cannot consent

If you cannot give your consent, either because you are unconscious or because your disability or illness means you cannot understand what you are being asked to agree to or are unable to express your views, doctors and other clinicians may need to decide about medical treatments on your behalf.

Any decision must be in your best interests as the individual patient concerned. This is not about what is in the best interests of any of your relatives or the doctors or the hospital or anyone else.

To find out what decision might be in your best interests, doctors may want to talk to people who know you, especially to find out if you have ever indicated anything to suggest what decision you might make now. To do so could involve doctors sharing some information about your current medical situation, in order for your family and friends (for example) to reflect on what your views might have been. The information that is shared should only be that needed to find out what your best interests might be.

If you have already recorded what you would want to happen if such a situation arises (for example, in an advance directive – see page 126), this should be respected and followed by the doctors involved in your care. You might want to place a copy of your wishes with your health records – perhaps with your GP if the surgery agrees.

There is more about consent in these situations in Chapter 8.

## Chapter 18

# Getting involved in the NHS

There are many ways you can be involved in, and influence, different parts of the NHS. Most NHS organisations want (and ask) members of the public to take part in some way. For example, the National Institute for Health and Clinical Excellence (NICE) has a Citizen's Council, drawn from different members of the public. To help with its overall policy approach, NICE asks its Citizens Council to debate some of the ethical issues about access to different health care services and treatments from the NHS.

Other NHS bodies, such as the National Patient Safety Agency, also look for lay members – people who aren't involved in this work professionally – to join committees looking at issues such as (for example) the information needed by patients and carers.

Most of these positions are unpaid, although you will receive expenses such as travel costs. These opportunities are usually advertised in national newspapers, such as *The Guardian*. There are other ways you can also become more involved, outlined below.

# Patient Forums

Each Primary Care Trust and NHS Trust must have a Patient Forum, which consists of members of the public. There must be at least seven Forum members but many involve 15–25 people. Members receive training to help them carry out their roles:

- to find out the views of their local communities about health services and make recommendations and reports based on these views;
- to make reports and recommendations on the range and day-to-day delivery of health services;
- to influence the design of and access to NHS services;
- to provide advice and information to patients and their carers about services;
- to monitor the effectiveness of local Patient Advice and Liaison Services (see Chapter 16).

Forums also hold public meetings that you can go to and share your views and experiences of the NHS locally. The Commission for Patient and Public Involvement in Health (CPPIH) is an independent body that has the overall responsibility for the 572 forums across England. Local not-for-profit organisations (voluntary organisations or charities) provide support to local Forums, under contract to the CPPIH. To find out about getting involved or for details of your local Forum, you can contact the CPPIH (address on page 269).

In 2004, the Government published proposals to change this system. This includes plans to abolish the CPPIH, although Patient Forums will continue. A new system of supporting Forums is being devised.

# Expert Patients Programme

The Government has told the NHS to actively involve people with chronic (long-term) health conditions in managing their illnesses. These include:

- arthritis
- epilepsy
- schizophrenia.

Over the last couple of years, the Department of Health has been developing the Expert Patients Programme for people with chronic conditions. It's based on studies that have found that it is often the person with the condition or illness who has the greatest expertise into what affects this and their overall health.

The Expert Patients Programme offers training sessions to people with chronic conditions, to help them learn about their condition and its symptoms in order to improve their confidence in dealing with it the best possible way. This might be about managing pain, reducing anxiety or finding ways to feel less tired. The sessions also look at diet, exercise and the best ways to talk to health care professionals. The courses take place over a six-week period, each session lasting two and a half hours.

The training sessions are run by other people who have long-term conditions. But they are not about replacing help from the NHS. You will still see your GP and hospital consultant, physiotherapist or dietitian as needed. Many people who have taken part have found that it helps them to have much more control, and a better say, over what happens.

Each Strategic Health Authority has to draw up plans to introduce the Programme in its area. This will be run by Primary Care Trusts, who have been told that the scheme must be available across England by

2008. To find out about taking part, you can contact the Expert Patients Programme at the address on page 273.

# NHS Patient Surveys

Every year a survey of NHS patients takes place. Some years it looks at particular types of services that only some people receive, such as cancer services; other years it looks at services that everyone receives, such as GPs. These surveys are carried out in each area by the local Primary Care Trusts.

Apart from this annual survey, individual surgeries, clinics, hospitals and other NHS services often run their own local surveys. Or there may be a 'comment card' available for you to complete. If you use a particular service, you might be asked to take part in a review. This will look at what is good about the service as it is at the moment as well as what might need to change for the future. Most research about NHS services involves seeking the views of patients and carers. An NHS Ethics Committee in each area looks at each research proposal before the go-ahead is given to talk with patients.

# Clinical trials

Many drug trials are carried out among patients. These trials can be run either by the NHS or by private drug (pharmaceutical) companies. The trials are usually the final stages in testing out drugs before it is finally agreed that they should be made more widely available. Or they may look at the effects of taking certain treatments, already available on prescription, over a period of time.

Typically the people taking part are divided into two groups: those who are given the drug or treatment to take, and those given a placebo. A placebo is something that looks the same as the drug but is made up of something else that is quite harmless. You will not know until the end of the trial whether you were taking the drug being tested or a placebo.

Some clinical trials might involve your attending a clinic or hospital for tests. For example, the trial could involve regular scans to see any changes in your brain (this is often carried out among people with a particular health condition, such as depression or a stroke). Another example is the work to find cures carried out with volunteer patients by the Common Cold Unit.

Your GP surgery may ask you to take part. Or you may see advertisements in national or local newspapers asking for volunteers. Either way it is up to you whether you take part – you are free to say no. Some trials offer you a payment, others do not; or you may be reimbursed for any expenses involved in taking part (such as the cost of travel to a clinic).

## Other involvement

Many people have been involved with the NHS in other ways, by volunteering or by raising money. Most NHS hospitals have benefited at some point from fundraising involving the help of former patients (and their families and friends) to buy specialist equipment, or perhaps refurbish parts of the hospital (such as waiting areas) or to raise funds to buy art and sculpture to display in the hospital.

Some hospitals have a 'Friends' organisation that you can join. They arrange events to raise money or to help support the hospital in other ways. The charities the British Red Cross and the Women's Royal Voluntary Service have traditionally been very involved with NHS hospitals. Volunteers for both organisations often run extra services for hospital patients, such as:

- café for patients and visitors;
- hospital shop;
- lending library.

Sometimes volunteers visit particular wards and, if patients are interested, will help with putting on make-up, styling hair, or painting their fingernails. For more information about volunteering, contact your local hospital, the British Red Cross or the Women's Royal Voluntary Service (addresses on pages 267 and 284).

# Campaigning

Many individuals, charities and support groups campaign for local and national changes to health services. For example, Age Concern England's recent campaigns include: raising the age at which women are invited for breast screening from 65 to 70 (page 17); changing how 'Do Not Resuscitate' decisions are made (page 207); and challenging age discrimination (page 224). Campaigns often begin with someone who is unhappy about a health care experience, contacting their MP or a national or local charity or support group to see if these concerns are shared. Some people decide to contact the media: if you do so, say clearly whether you agree to their reporting your story using your real name and details.

Not all stories are reported in the media, nor do charities or local support groups take up every issue. This may be because they have different priorities; not enough time or money to take it up; or they don't share your view that this is an important issue. If this happens, you may want to rethink your approach. Successful campaigning – both national and local – tends to take more than your simply believing you have a good case. You need to be able to persuade others that change is needed. Although it can take time to achieve, though, it is worth persevering.

## Chapter 19

# Keeping up to date with change

As this book may have already made clear to you, changes to how and what the NHS does can happen at any time. In recent years there have been lots of changes to the NHS, particularly in terms of:

- new organisations;
- different responsibilities;
- quality and monitoring of services;
- where you can go for help from the NHS;
- how quickly you are seen.

There is no doubt that more change will follow – and keep on coming. The NHS has been changing since it began in 1948. There is no reason to think it will stop now.

In some organisations, keeping up to date with change in the NHS and with health care services in general is a full-time job. For the rest of us, it can be difficult to know where to go and how to find out what the NHS does *now*. But there are lots of ways we can keep up to date – at least with the parts of the NHS that affect us the most.

Some people who are part of campaigning groups may be involved in local or national networks that keep them up to date with the latest developments by email, telephone or letter. Others may want to look at specialist health journals, such as the *British Medical Journal* (*BMJ*) or the *Health Service Journal* (*HSJ*). If you don't want to buy these you may be able to read them at your local library if it has a subscription to them.

There is a lot of information available on the Internet. The Department of Health has its own website, as does NHS Direct (see pages 270 and 279) and many of the other organisations listed in the Appendix. There are also many local websites – for example, your local Primary Care Trust may have a website. (See also page 27.)

Sometimes, newspapers and other media (TV or radio) report changes in the NHS. Although this may alert you to change, you may find that these reports don't give you enough information about what the changes mean for you as a patient. You may need to go elsewhere to find out more.

Having access to accurate and detailed information is an incredibly important part of understanding what the NHS is doing, should do, won't do and can't do. Charities such as Age Concern England help explain these changes as they are happening by producing information sheets, factsheets and policy papers. You can also contact them by telephone with other queries (see page 264).

If you belong to an organisation that specialises in a particular health condition or disability, such as Arthritis Care, Cancer BACUP or the Alzheimer's Society, you will probably receive regular newsletters and other information from them. This will also help keep you up to date with the things affecting people with those illnesses and disabilities.

Of course, none of this may interest you. The last thing you might want to do is try to keep tabs on the NHS. So perhaps the most important lesson is not to be surprised that something has changed when you next come to use any of the huge range of NHS services. Your last experience of the NHS may be quite different from your next one.

## Appendix

# Useful addresses

Only a few self-help or support organisations are listed in this Appendix. For information about the many others that exist, ask at your local library for a directory such as *Charity Choice* (published by Waterlow Professional Publishing) or *Voluntary Agencies Directory* (published by the National Council for Voluntary Organisations).

**Note**: telephone codes/call charges are: 01, area code; 02, area code; 07, mobile rate; 080, free; 084 local rate; 087, national rate; 09, premium rate

**Action for Victims of Medical Accidents (AvMA)**
44 High Street
Croydon CR0 1YB
Tel: 020 8688 9555
Email: avma.co@virgin.net
Website: www.avma.org.uk
*For advice after a medical accident.*

**Age Concern Information Line**
0800 00 99 66
*See also page 285 for more information about Age Concern.*

## Alliance of Private Sector Chiropody and Podiatry Practitioners
PO Box 10289
Rowley Regis
West Midlands B65 0WA
Tel: 0121 559 2772
Website: www.thealliancepsp.com
*For information about the training and registration of their chiropodist and podiatrist members.*

## Alzheimer's Society
Gordon House
10 Greencoat Place
London SW1P 1PH
Helpline: 0845 300 0336 (Mon–Fri, 8.30am–6.30pm; a simultaneous language translation service is available on this number)
Website: www.alzheimers.org.uk
*For information about Alzheimer's disease and other dementias.*

## Associated Chiropodists and Podiatrists Union
(formerly **Association of Chiropodists and Podiatrists)**
Suite 14, Anglesey Business Centre
Anglesey Road
Burton on Trent
Staffordshire DE14 3NT
Tel: 01283 741174
*For information about the training and registration of their chiropodist and podiatrist members.*

## Association of Professional Music Therapists
26 Hamlyn Road
Glastonbury
Somerset BA6 8HT
Tel: 01458 834919

Website: www.apmt.org
*The professional organisation of music therapists.*

**British Association of Arts Therapists**
Southampton Place Business Centre
16–19 Southampton Place
London WC1A 2AJ
Tel: 020 7745 7262
Website: www.baat.org
*The professional organisation of arts therapists.*

**British Association for Counselling and Psychotherapy**
BACP House
35–37 Albert Street
Rugby
Warwickshire CV21 2SG
Tel: 0870 443 5252
Website: www.bacp.co.uk
*To find a trained counsellor near you.*

**British Association of Dramatherapists**
41 Broomhouse Lane
London SW6 3DP
Tel: 020 7731 0160
*The professional association of dramatherapists.*

**British Chiropody Podiatry Association**
The New Hall
149 Bath Road
Maidenhead
Berkshire SL6 4LA
Tel: 01628 632449
Website: www.bcha-uk.org

For information about the training and registration of chiropodists and podiatrists.

**British Deaf Association**

1–3 Worship Street

London EC2A 2AB

Helpline (voice): 0870 770 3300

   (text): 0800 652 2965

Website: www.bda.org.uk

For information about services for deaf people.

**British Organ Donor Society (BODY)**

Balsham

Cambridge CB1 6DL

Tel: 01223 893636

Website: www.argonet.co.uk/body

For information about donating organ(s).

**British Red Cross**

9 Grosvenor Crescent

London SW1X 7EJ

Tel: 020 7235 5454

Website: www.redcross.org.uk

For the hire/loan of equipment; it publishes The Emergency Multilingual Phrasebook of medical terms.

**British Trust for Conservations Volunteers (BTCV)**

The Conservation Centre

163 Balby Road

Balby

Doncaster DN4 0RH

Tel: 01302 572200

Website: www.btcv.org.uk

To find out about Green Gyms in your area.

## Charles Russell Solicitors

fao Rowena Hill/Edwina Rawson
8–10 New Fetter Lane
London EC4A 1RS
Tel: 020 7203 5000
*For obtaining compensation regarding Creutzfeld–Jakob disease.*

## Chartered Society of Physiotherapy

14 Bedford Row
London WC1R 4ED
Tel: 020 7306 6666
Website: www.csp.org.uk
*The professional organisation of physiotherapists.*

## Child Poverty Action Group (CPAG)

94 White Lion Street
London N1 9PE
Tel: 020 7837 7979
Website: www.cpag.org.uk
*For a copy of its publication* The Welfare Rights Handbook.

## Choose and Book

Email: chooseandbook@npfit.nhs.uk
Website: www.chooseandbook.nhs.uk
*For information about the new system of booking a hospital appointment yourself.*

## Cinnamon Trust

The National Charity for the elderly and their pets
Foundry House
Foundry Square
Hayle
Cornwall TR27 4HH
Tel: 01736 757900

Website: www.cinnamon.org
*Helps with looking after pets of people in hospital.*

**CJD Support Network**
Birchwood, Heath Top
Ashley Heath
Market Drayton
Shropshire TF9 4QR
Helpline: 01630 673973
Email: support@cjdsupport.net
Website: www.cjdsupport.net
*For obtaining compensation regarding Creutzfeld–Jakob disease.*

**College of Occupational Therapists**
106–114 Borough High Street
London SE1 1LB
Tel: 020 7357 7480
Website: www.cot.co.uk
*The professional organisation of occupational therapists.*

**Commission for Patient and Public Involvement in Health (CPPIH)**
Help Desk
7th Floor, 120 Edmund Street
Birmingham B3 2ES
Tel: 0845 120 7111
Textphone: 0845 120 7113
Website: www.cppih.org
*For information about Patient Forums.*

**Commission for Social Care Inspection**
33 Greycoat Street
London SW1P 2QF
Customer services helpline: 0845 015 0120

Website: www.csci.org.uk
*The official body regulating care homes and agencies that provide nurses or care workers who carry out personal tasks.*

**Counsel and Care**
Twyman House
16 Bonny Street
London NW1 9PG
Advice line: 0845 300 7585 (Mon–Fri, 9am–1pm)
Website: www.counselandcare.org.uk
*For information on finding and paying for a care home.*

**Cruse Bereavement Care**
Cruse House
126 Sheen Road
Richmond
Surrey TW9 1UR
Tel: 0870 167 1677
Website: www.crusebereavement.org.uk
*For bereavement counselling and advice.*

**Dementia Services Development Centre**
Iris Murdoch Building
University of Stirling
Stirling FK9 4LA
Tel: 01786 467740
Website: www.dementia.stir.ac.uk
*Researches into ways to help support people with dementia.*

**Department of Health**
PO Box 777
London SE1 6XH
Helpline: 0800 555 777
Tel: 020 7210 4850

Textphone: 020 7210 5025

Website: www.dh.gov.uk

*For information about NHS services and health issues.*

**To order health literature**

Tel: 0800 555 777

**For information on NHS charges**

Tel: 0800 9177 771

Website www.dh.gov.uk/charges

**For information about NHS services for visitors from overseas**

Room 4W04b

Quarry House

Quarry Hill

Leeds LS2 7UE

Tel: 0113 254 5819

Website: www.dh.gov.uk/overseas

**Department of Health, Social Services and Public Safety**

Senior Medical Officer

Room C3.7

Castle Buildings, Stormont

Belfast BT4 3RA

*For donating one's body for medical research in Northern Ireland.*

**Depression Alliance**

35 Westminster Bridge Road

London SE1 7JB

Tel: 0845 123 23 20

*For information and advice about depression.*

**Diabetes UK Careline**

10 Parkway

London NW1 7AA

Tel: 0845 120 2960 (weekdays, 9am–5pm; translation service available)

Website: www.diabetes.org.uk

*For information and advice about diabetes.*

## Disability Rights Commission (DRC)

DRC Helpline

FREEPOST MID02164

Stratford upon Avon

Warwickshire CV37 9BR

Tel: 08457 622633

Textphone: 08457 622644 } (Mon–Fri, 8am–8pm)

Website: www.drc-gb.org

*Government-sponsored centre with publications and information on the Disability Discrimination Act.*

## Disabled Living Foundation

380–384 Harrow Road

London W9 2HU

Helpline: 0845 130 9177 (Mon–Fri,10am–1pm)

Tel: 020 7289 6111

Textphone: 020 7432 8009

Fax: 020 7266 2922

Website: www.dlf.org.uk

*Information for disabled and older people on all kinds of equipment that will promote their independence and quality of life.*

## Driver and Vehicle Licensing Agency (DVLA)

Swansea SA99 1BA

Tel: 0870 240 0010

Textphone: 01792 782756

Website: www.dvla.gov.uk

*Government office; offers advice to drivers with medical conditions.*

## Elderly Accommodation Counsel

3rd Floor

89 Albert Embankment

London SE1 7TP

Tel: 020 7820 1343

Website: www.housingcare.org

*For their information sheet about making a complaint.*

## Expert Patients Programme

Tel: 0845 606 6040

Website: www.expertpatients.nhs.uk

*To find out about becoming an 'expert patient'.*

## General Dental Council

37 Wimpole Street

London W1G 8DQ

Tel: 020 7887 3800

Textphone: 020 7887 3800 (via Typetalk)

Website: www.gdc-uk.org

*The official regulating body of dentists.*

## General Medical Council

178 Great Portland Street

London W1W 5JE

Tel (concerning a doctor's fitness to practise): 020 7915 3603

Website: www.gmc-uk.org

*The official regulating body of doctors.*

*The GMC's Manchester office also deals with some fitness to practice issues:*

St James Building

79 Oxford Street

Manchester M1 6FQ

Tel: 0845 357 8001

## General Optical Council
41 Harley Street
London W1G 8DJ
Tel: 020 7580 3898
Website: www.optical.org
*The official regulating body of optometrists and dispensing opticians, both individuals and organisations.*

## Guide Dogs for the Blind Association
Burghfield Common
Reading RG7 3YG
Tel: 0870 600 2323
Website: www.guidedogs.org.uk
*For information about guide dogs.*

## HM Inspector of Anatomy (for England, Wales and Scotland)
Room 611
Wellington House
135–155 Waterloo Road
London SE1 8UG
Tel: 020 7972 4551/4342
*To donate one's body for research or anatomical examination.*

## Health Professions Council
Park House
184 Kennington Park Road
London SE11 4BU
Tel: 020 7582 0866
Website: www.hpc-uk.org
*The body for registering therapists such as occupational therapists and speech and language therapists.*

## Health Service Ombudsman
Millbank Tower
*274*

Millbank

London SW1P 4QP

Tel: 0845 015 4033

Email: OHSC.Enquiries@ombudsman.gsi.gov.uk

Website: www.ombudsman.org.uk

*To make a complaint about or appeal against a decision made by the NHS.*

### Healthcare Commission

FREEPOST NAT 18958

Complaints Investigation Team

Manchester M1 9XZ

Helpline: 0845 601 3012

E-mail: complaints@healthcarecommission.org.uk

Website: www.healthcarecommission.org.uk

*Inspects NHS services in England and Wales, and regulates private and voluntary health care services in England.*

### HealthSpace

Website: www.healthspace.nhs.uk

*An online service provided by the NHS for people aged 16 or over in England. If you want, you can use this secure website to keep a record of your health details.*

### Hearing Dogs for Deaf People

The Grange

Wycombe Road

Saunderton

Princes Risborough

Buckinghamshire HP27 9NS

Tel: 01844 348 100 (voice and text)

Website: www.hearing-dogs.co.uk

*For information about Hearing Dogs.*

**Help the Aged**
207–221 Pentonville Road
London N1 9UZ
Tel: 0808 800 6565 (Helpline Mon–Fri, 9am-4pm)
Website: helptheaged.org.uk
*For information and leaflets about preventing falls, as well as a wide range of other information for older people.*

**Help the Hospices**
Hospice House
34–44 Britannia Street
London
WC1X 9JG
*or*
***St Christopher's Hospice***
51–59 Lawrie Park Road
Sydenham
London SE26 6DZ
Hospice Information
Tel: 0870 903 3903 (Mon–Fri, office hours)
*For information about hospice care.*

**Hepatitis C Trust**
27 Crosby Row
London SE1 3YD
Tel: 020 7089 6220
*For information about hepatitis C.*

**Home Office**
***Coroner's Section***
5th Floor
Allington Towers
19 Allington Street

London SW1E 5EB
Tel: 020 7035 5530/5531
Website: www.homeoffice.gov.uk
*For the leaflet* When Sudden Death Occurs.

### Drugs Branch
Tel: 020 7273 3806
*For information about medicines/drugs that you are not allowed to take out of the UK.*

### Information Commissioner
Wycliffe House
Water Lane
Wilmslow
Cheshire SK9 5AF
Tel: 01625 545700
*The organisation responsible for Freedom of Information Act issues.*

### Institute of Chiropodists & Podiatrists
27 Wright Street
Southport
Merseyside PR9 0TL
Tel: 08700 110 305
Website: www.inst-chiropodist.org.uk
*For information about the training and registration of chiropodists and podiatrists.*

### Limbless Association
Rehabilitation Centre
Roehampton Lane
London SW15 5PR
Tel: 020 8788 1777
Website: www.limbless-association.org
*For information about obtaining/using a wheelchair.*

## Macmillan Cancer Relief

89 Albert Embankment

London SE1 7UQ

Macmillan CancerLine: 0808 808 2020 (Mon–Fri, 9am–6pm)

Textphone: 0808 808 0121

Website: www.macmillan.org.uk

*For specialist nursing services.*

## Marie Curie Cancer Care

89 Albert Embankment

London SE1 7TP

Tel (for details of the Marie Curie Cancer Care Nursing Service):

01495 740845 (Mon–Fri, 9am–5pm)

Website: www.mariecurie.org.uk

*For specialist nursing services.*

## Mental Health Foundation

83 Victoria Street

London SW1H 0HW

Tel: 020 7802 0300

Website: www.mentalhealth.org.uk

*For information about mental illnesses.*

## MIND

15–19 Broadway

London E15 4BQ

Information helpline: 0845 766 0163 (Mon–Fri, 9.15am–5.15pm)

Tel: 020 8519 2122

Website: www.mind.org.uk

*For information on solicitors specialising in mental health law, and about financial help with these costs; and advocacy support.*

**Monitor**

4 Matthew Parker Street

London SW1H 9NL

Tel: 020 7340 2400

Website: www.monitor-nhsft.gov.uk

*The Independent Regulator for NHS Foundation Trusts.*

**NHS Direct**

Helpline: 0845 4647

Textphone: 0845 606 4647

*24-hour helpline offering confidential health care advice, information and referral service 365 days of the year.*

**NHS Direct Online**

Website: www.nhsdirect.nhs.uk

Wales: www.nhsdirect.wales.nhs.uk

*Health care advice and information 365 days of the year.*

**NHS Organ Donor Register**

Tel: 0845 6060 4000

Website: www.uktransplant.org.uk

*For information about donating organ(s).*

**National Blood Service**

Tel: 0845 771 1711

Website: www.blood.co.uk

*To find out about becoming a blood donor.*

**National Cochlear Implant Users Association (NCIUA)**

PO Box 260

High Wycombe

Buckinghamshire HP11 1FA

Website: www.nciua.demon.co.uk

*For information about cochlear implants.*

## National Federation of Shopmobility UK
The Hawkins Suite
Enham Place
Enham Alamein
Andover
Hampshire SP11 6JS
Tel: 08456 442 446
Website: www.justmobility.co.uk/shop
*For the loan of wheelchairs/powered scooters to use when shopping.*

## National Osteoporosis Society
Camerton
Bath BA2 0PJ
Tel: 01761 471771
Website: www.nos.org.uk
*For information and advice about osteoporosis.*

## National Patient Safety Agency (NPSA)
4–8 Maple Street
London W1T 5HD
Tel: 020 7927 9500 (general enquiries)
      0800 015 2536 (to make a report)
*To raise concerns about treatment.*

## Nursing and Midwifery Council
Fitness to Practise Directorate
23 Portland Place
London W1N 4JT
Tel: 020 7333 6572
Website: www.nmc-uk.org
*The official/registering body of nurses and midwives.*

## Royal College of Speech and Language Therapists
2 White Hart Yard
London SE1 1NX
Tel: 020 7378 1200
Website: www.rcslt.org
*The professional organisation of speech and language therapists.*

## Royal National Institute of the Blind (RNIB)
105 Judd Street
London WC1H 9NE
Helpline: 0845 766 9999
Website: www.rnib.org.uk
*For a range of information and services for people who are blind or partially sighted.*

## Royal National Institute for Deaf People (RNID)
19–23 Featherstone Street
London EC1Y 8SL
Information Line: 0808 808 0123
Textphone: 0808 808 9000
Website: www.rnid.org.uk
*For a range of information and services for people who are deaf or hard of hearing, including those listed below.*

### *Tinnitus helpline*
Tel: 0808 808 6666
Textphone: 0808 808 0007

### *RNID Typetalk*
Textphone: 0800 500 888
Tel: 0800 7311 888
Website: www.typetalk.org

## Royal Pharmaceutical Society of Great Britain

1 Lambeth High Street
London SE1 7JN
Tel: 020 7735 9141
Website: www.rpsgb.org.uk
*The official body of pharmacists in the UK.*

## Samaritans

Tel: 08457 90 90 90 (24 hours a day, all year round)
Website: www.samaritans.org.uk
*24-hour helpline for people needing to talk. Also available by personal visit, by letter or by email.*
*by personal visit*: see the phone book for your local branch
*by letter*: Chris, PO Box 9090, Stirling FK8 2SA (remember to give your address if you want a reply)
*by email*: jo@samaritans.org.uk

## SANE

1st Floor
Cityside House
40 Adler Street
London E1 1EE
Saneline: 0845 767 8000 (noon–2am every day)
Website: www.sane.org.uk
*For information about schizophrenia.*

## Shopmobility

see National Federation of Shopmobility UK

## Skipton Fund

PO Box 50107
London SW1H 0YF
Tel: 020 7808 1160
Email: apply@skiptonfund.org

Website: www.skiptonfund.org.uk
*For obtaining compensation for contracting hepatitis C through NHS blood and blood-related products.*

**Society of Chiropodists and Podiatrists**
1 Fellmonger's Path
Tower Bridge Road
London SE1 3LY
Tel: 020 7234 8620
Website: www.scpod.org
*For information about the training and registration of chiropodists and podiatrists.*

**The Stationery Office**
TSO
PO Box 29
Norwich NR3 1GN
Tel: 0870 600 5522
Fax: 0870 600 5533
Website: www.hmso.gov.uk
*To order government publications, including reports by the Health Service Ombudsman.*

**Time Banks UK**
City Works
Alfred Street
Gloucester GL1 4DF
Tel: 01452 541439
Website: www.timebanks.co.uk
*To find out about the Time Bank schemes locally.*

**United Kingdom Home Care Association (UKHCA)**
42b Banstead Road
Carshalton Beeches

Surrey SM5 3NW

Tel: 020 8288 1551

Website: www.ukhca.co.uk

*An organisation whose member organisations provide care at home.*

**United Kingdom Transplant**

Website: www.uktransplant.org.uk

*For information about donating blood, organs and tissues.*

**vCJD Trust**

Website: www.vCJD.co.uk

*For obtaining compensation regarding Creutzfeld–Jakob disease.*

**Women's Royal Voluntary Service (WRVS)**

Garden House

Milton Hill

Steventon

Abingdon

Oxfordshire OX13 6AD

Tel: 01235 442900

Website: www.wrvs.org.uk

*Volunteer services such as hospital shop and lending library.*

# About Age Concern

Age Concern is the UK's largest organisation working for and with older people to enable them to make more of life. We are a federation of over 400 independent charities that share the same name, values and standards.

We believe that ageing is a normal part of life, and that later life should be fulfilling, enjoyable and productive. We enable older people by providing services and grants, researching their needs and opinions, influencing government and media, and through other innovative and dynamic projects.

Every day we provide vital services, information and support to thousands of older people of all ages and backgrounds.

Age Concern also works with many older people from disadvantaged or marginalised groups, such as those living in rural areas or black and minority ethnic elders.

Age Concern is dependent on donations, covenants and legacies.

**Age Concern England**
1268 London Road
London SW16 4ER
Tel: 020 8765 7200
Fax: 020 8765 7211
Website:
www.ageconcern.org.uk

**Age Concern Scotland**
113 Rose Street
Edinburgh EH2 3DT
Tel: 0131 220 3345
Fax: 0131 220 2779
Website:
www.ageconcernscotland.org.uk

**Age Concern Cymru**
Units 13 & 14 Neptune Court
Vanguard Way
Cardiff CF24 5PJ
Tel: 029 2043 1555
Website: www.accymru.org.uk

**Age Concern Northern Ireland**
3 Lower Crescent
Belfast BT7 1NR
Tel: 028 9024 5729
Fax: 028 9023 5497
Website: www.ageconcernni.org

# Publications from Age Concern Books

## Your Rights: A guide to money benefits for older people
*Sally West*

A highly acclaimed guide to the state benefits available to older people. It contains current information on Income Support, Housing Benefit and retirement pensions, among other matters, and provides advice on how to claim.

For more information, please telephone 0870 44 22 120.

## Their Rights: Advance directives and living wills explored
*Kevin Kendrick and Simon Robinson*

In recent decades, 'living wills' or 'advance directives' have been actively promoted as a means of giving people choice and control about medical treatment, particularly at the end of life. This book explains the law relating to advance directives and illustrates decisions about treatment with case studies.

£9.99 0-86242-244-2

## The Carer's Handbook: What to do and who to turn to
*Marina Lewycka*

The handbook has been written to help readers through difficult caring situations, including emergencies, and covers sorting out priorities, arranging care, identifying the right sources of professional help, considering options, and arranging financial matters. It is an invaluable reference point.

£6.99 0-86242-366-X

## Caring for someone in their own home
*Helen Howard*

This book is full of practical information about dealing with the everyday business of caring for someone in their home, from medication to moving and handling someone without damaging your back. It contains information on daily essentials, financial and legal aspects to caring,

dealing with the health and social care system, and looking at longer-term care. The book is here to help you as a carer: it could be one of the best ways of helping the person you are caring for.
£9.99 0-86242-362-7

---

If you would like to order any of these titles, please write to the address below, enclosing a cheque or money order for the appropriate amount (plus £1.99 p&p for one book; for additional books please add 75p per book up to a maximum of £7.50) made payable to Age Concern England. Credit card orders may be made on 0870 44 22 120. Books can also be ordered online at www.ageconcern.org.uk/shop

**Age Concern Books**
Units 5 and 6 Industrial Estate
Brecon
Powys LD3 8LA

---

## Bulk order discounts

Age Concern Books is pleased to offer a discount on orders totalling 50 or more copies of the same title. For details, please contact Age Concern Books on 0870 44 22 120.

## Customised editions

Age Concern Books is pleased to offer a free 'customisation' service for anyone wishing to purchase 500 or more copies of a title. This gives you the option to have a unique front cover design featuring your organisation's logo and corporate colours, or adding your logo to the current cover design. You can also insert an additional four pages of text for a small additional fee. Existing clients include many prominent names in British industry, retailing and finance, the trades unions, educational establishments, public, private and voluntary sectors, and welfare associations. For full details, please contact Sue Henning, Age Concern Books, Astral House, 1268 London Road, London SW16 4ER. Fax: 020 8765 7211. Email: hennins@ace.org.uk

Visit our Website at: www.ageconcern.org.uk/shop

# Age Concern Information Line/ Factsheets subscription

Age Concern produces more than 45 comprehensive factsheets designed to answer many of the questions older people (or those advising them) may have. These include money and benefits, health, community care, leisure and education, and housing. For up to five free factsheets, telephone 0800 00 99 66 (8am–7pm, seven days a week, every week of the year). Alternatively, you may prefer to write to:

Age Concern, FREEPOST (SWB 30375), ASHBURTON, Devon TQ13 7ZZ.

For professionals working with older people, the factsheets are available on an annual subscription service, which includes updates throughout the year. For further details and costs of the subscription, please contact Age Concern at the above Freepost address.

*We hope that this publication has been useful to you. If so, we would very much like to hear from you. Alternatively, if you feel that we could add or change anything, please write and tell us, using the following Freepost address:*
*Age Concern, FREEPOST CN1794, London SW16 4BR.*

# INDEX

abroad, living 35, 191, 192–195
Accident & Emergency Units 24, 29–30, 151, 248
accidents
    medical 243
    road 160, 203
Acts of Parliament 3, 4–7, 44
acupuncture 43, 44
adaptations, house 81–83, 99, 100, 172
Adults with Incapacity (Scotland) Act 2000 129
advance decisions/advance directives/Living Wills 118, 126–129, 157–158, 203, 255
advance statements 126, 129–131
advocates 121
age discrimination 13, 15, 261
agencies, private nursing 46
aids see equipment
Alder Hey Hospital 217, 220
Alzheimer's disease 110; see also dementia
Alzheimer's Society 7, 111, 112, 128, 263
ambulance services 3, 30–32, 166, 169, 183
angina 17
antidepressants 105
appointments 22–23, 153–155, 221
Aricept 111
art therapists 80, 84, 241
arthritis, people with 7, 46, 263
artificial hydration and nutrition 8, 184, 212–213
assisted suicide 209–210
asthma, people with 46
audiology tests 73
auto-transfusion 202–203

benefits 39, 68, 71, 131, 163–164, 187–188, 215

bereavement, dealing with 220
'best practice' 4, 10–11
Bland, Tony 8, 212
blindness see eyesight, loss of
Blood, Diane 8
blood donation 197–198, 201–203, 242
Blue Badge parking scheme 68, 131
Bournewood case 124–125
British Red Cross 32, 248, 260–261
Burke, Mr 130, 211

campaigning groups 261, 262
cancers 17–18, 55, 85, 152
    and palliative care 206, 207
    screening services 17, 38, 261
car accidents, treatment after 160, 203
care homes
    charges 10, 97, 174, 222
    dentistry services 53
    equipment and aids 100
    funeral arrangements 219–220
    moving to 174, 176
    and NHS care 35, 41, 45, 178–180, 186, 187–188
    and palliative care 206
    temporary stays in 173, 174
    and use of neuroleptics 112
    see also nursing homes
Care Trusts 3
case law 3, 7–9, 184, 211, 212, 213
cataracts 61–62, 64, 67, 70
    removal of 151–152, 153, 165
charges, NHS 11–12, 21–22, 43, 45, 92–99
charities viii, 7, 175, 250, 260, 263
chemists see pharmacists
'Child B' 8–9
chiropodists/chiropody 34, 40, 44, 87, 132–133, 134, 135–139, 242
    private 139–140

Cinnamon Trust 165
clinical negligence claims 230, 243
clinical trials 259–260
cochlear implants 78
cognitive behavioural therapy
    105–106
community health services 40–41
community matrons 46
community mental health/psychiatric
    nurses 41, 114–115
compensation claims 230, 242–243
complaints systems
    care homes 180
    Foundation Trusts 230–231
    individual professionals 236–242
    local authority 175
    NHS 10–11, 12, 37, 91, 175, 189,
        218, 223–230
    see also Health Service
        Ombudsman; Healthcare
        Commission
complementary therapies 43
confidentiality 18, 19, 20; see also
    records, health
consent 123–124, 157
    and 'mental capacity' 124–126,
        159
consultants 39, 55, 67, 73
    and second opinions 40, 250
contact lenses 21, 62, 63, 66,
    94–95
continence services 15, 41–42, 86,
    99, 184
continuing NHS health care 183–189
corneal transplants 200, 201
coronary heart disease 17
coroners 215, 216–217, 218–219,
    245
Coughlan, Pamela 9
counselling services 80, 105–106
    bereavement 220
    private 106–107
Creutzfeldt–Jakob disease 242–243
criminal offences 245, 253–254
crisis cards 118

Data Protection Act 1998 250, 251,
    252
day care services 113–114
deafness see hearing difficulties
death 205
    certifying and registering 214–216
    and health records 252
    and moving a body abroad 219
    see also funeral arrangements
decision-making 249–250
    and 'mental capacity' 125–126,
        210
    see also advance decisions
delusions 103, 116, 117
dementia, people with 16, 102, 103,
    131
    communicating with 115
    and depression 109, 110
    getting a diagnosis 110–111
    and medication 111–112
    support services 112, 113–115
dentistry 2, 12, 21, 34, 48–51, 60
    anaesthetics 59–60
    bridges and crowns 53, 54, 56
    charges 49, 53, 56–57, 93–94
    check-ups/examinations 51,
        54–55
    complaints about 236, 237,
        239–241
    cosmetic treatments 53
    dentures 54, 56–57
    emergency care 51–52, 56
    home visits 49, 52–53
    in hospital 59
    and insurance 59
    mobile services 53
    nurses and assistants 55
    out-of-hours services 52
    private 52, 53–54, 58–59
    referrals 55
    registration 56
    'salaried' 49
    treatment plans 53, 54
depression, people with 16, 86, 102,
    103–104

depression (*cont*)
  and dementia 109, 110
  getting help and support 104–108
  as side effect of medication 104
diabetes, people with 18, 46, 141, 184
  eye-screening for 65, 69–70
  and foot care 135, 136–137
diabetic retinopathy 62, 70
Diagnostic and Treatment Centres 70
Directions 4, 5, 9–10
Disability Discrimination Act 1995 68–69, 71, 76, 249
Disability Rights Commission 208, 213
discrimination
  age 13, 15, 224, 261
  disability 68–69
district nurses 2, 34, 41, 44, 45, 99
'do-not-resuscitate' 207–208, 261
doctors, NHS *see* GPs
doctors, private 46–47, 245
donepezil 111
donors/donations
  of body to medical science 203–204
  *see also* blood donation; organ donation; tissue donation
drama therapists 80, 84, 241
driving 68, 131
drugs *see* medication

electro-convulsive therapy 122
emergency services 24, 30–32
'enough treatment' 6
epilepsy 16
equipment 15, 42, 82, 99–101, 184, 221
European health insurance cards 191, 192
euthanasia 209–110
Exelon 111
Expert Patients Programme 258–259
eye problems 66–67; *see also* eyesight

eyesight
  and diabetes 65, 69–70
  and driving 68
  laser treatment for 61, 70
  loss of 67–69, 71
  problems with 61–62
  professionals 63–64
  tests 11–12, 21, 63, 64–66
falls clinics viii, 16, 86–88, 137, 139
flu vaccinations 16, 20–21
foot care 134–135, 136–137; *see* chiropodists; nail-cutting services
Foundation Trusts 3, 230–231, 232
frames, walking 82, 101
funeral arrangements 215, 216, 219–220

galantamine 111
gay couples: and 'next-of-kin' 159
General Medical Council 237, 238–239, 244; *see also* Burke
General Optical Council 241
general practitioners *see* GPs
geriatricians 109
glasses *see* spectacles
glaucoma 62, 64
government policy decisions 4, 11–12
GPs/GP services/surgeries 2, 12, 24, 28, 34–35, 36–39, 42, 248
  appointments 22–23, 36–37
  changing practices 37
  complaints about 229, 236, 238–239
  home visits 42–43
  out-of-hours services 24, 28, 44
  referrals 38, 39–42, 152
  registering with 35–36
  removal from list 37–38
  second opinions 40, 250
  with Special Interests (GPwSI) 40
Guidance 4, 5, 9–10
guide dogs 69

hallucinations 116, 117
handrails 82–83, 99

health checks, annual 21, 38
Health Professions Council (HPC) 80,
    83, 84, 85, 133, 241, 244
Health Protection Agency 2
Health Service Ombudsman 184,
    186, 187, 189, 233, 234–236
health visitors 41, 44, 239
Healthcare Commission 10–11, 60,
    70, 90, 156, 228, 230, 231–234,
    244, 245
HealthSpace 27–28
hearing aids 73, 74–75
hearing difficulties/deafness, people
    with 71, 72, 85
    and cochlear implants 78
    and lip-reading 77
    and sign language 77
    telephones 99
    tests for 73, 74–75
    textphones 26, 77–78
    tinnitus 76
hearing dogs 76–77
heart disease, coronary 17
hepatitis C 242
hernia repairs 165
hip protectors 87–88
hip replacements 198
holidaymakers (in UK) 28, 37, 190
    non-UK citizens 191–192
home visits
    dentists 49, 52–53
    GPs 42–43
    opticians 65
    for people with dementia 114
homoeopathy 43
hospice services 41, 206, 207
hospitals 2, 3, 15, 34, 247–248
    Accident & Emergency 24, 29–30,
        151, 248
    admission to 151–152
    appointments 22–23, 153–155
    car parking 162–163
    Choose and Book system
        153–155
    and confidentiality 160

consenting to treatment see
    consent
day patients 113–114, 150, 165
and deaths 218–219, 220, 222
discharge from 166–175, 177, 247
ear, nose and throat departments
    73
eye services 67, 70
food 160–161
'Friends' organisations 260
in-patients 150
Minor Injuries Units 24, 32
mixed wards 160
moving between 166
orthopaedic departments 134
out-patients 150, 166
'pay beds' 244
private 176–177
psychiatric 109
radio services 162
refusal to leave 175–176
religious/spiritual needs 161–162
and road accident victims 160,
    203
and social services 165
and state benefits 163–164
targets 152–155
telephones 162
televisions 162
travel costs 95–96
visitors 163
Human Rights Act 1998 13, 161,
    211–212, 253

incontinence 41; see also continence
    services
Independent Complaints Advocacy
    Service 228, 229, 232
Independent Regulator 231
information 247–248, 262–263
    for non-English speakers 248–249
    see also records, health
inoculations 38; see also
    vaccinations
inquests 245

insurance, health 43, 47, 59, 86, 177
and road accidents 160
for health care abroad 191
'integrated' services viii, 15, 87
intermediate care services 15, 41,
85, 89–90, 176
Internet, the 263; see also NHS
Direct Online
interpreters 155, 249

Jehovah's Witnesses 202

legislation see Acts of Parliament;
case law
Lewy body dementia 110; see also
dementia
life-prolonging treatments 211–214
life-support machines 213–214
lip-reading courses 77
'Living Wills' see advance decisions
lobotomies 122

Macmillan nurses 41, 207
macular degeneration 62
Marie Curie nurses 207
marriages, death-bed 221
Medi-centres 24
medical records 193, 250–255
medical reports, charges for 43
medication (drugs) 143–144
checks on 21
and clinical trials 259–260
collecting 145
large-print labels 145
'over-the-counter' 141, 142
psychiatric 122
side effects of 104, 109, 112
taking abroad 147–148
see also prescriptions
memory loss 110
'mental capacity' 125
and consent 124–126, 159
Mental Capacity Bill 128, 129, 210
mental health services 2, 3, 14, 16
Mental Health Trusts 3

Mental Health Act 117, 118–119, 124
Mental Health Act Commission 122
Mental Health Review Tribunal 121,
122
mental illness 102–103
and disability benefits 131
and medication 121–122
see also dementia; schizophrenia;
'sectioning'
midwives, complaints about 239
MIND 121, 128
'Miss B' 8, 130, 213
Monitor 231
motor neurone disease 8, 17, 84,
209
multiple sclerosis (MS) 16, 84
music therapists 80, 84, 115, 241

nail-cutting services 133, 135,
138–139
National Health Service
core principles 13, 14
core standards 4, 10–11, 19–20
patient involvement 256–261
patients' rights 18, 19
staff rights 22–23
targets 11, 12
see also entries beginning NHS
National Institute for Health and
Clinical Excellence (NICE) 2, 4,
10, 88, 105, 111, 136–137
Citizens' Council 256
guidance on dentistry 51, 55
National Patient Safety Agency 11,
246, 256
National Service Frameworks 13–18,
46
negligence claims 230, 243
neuroleptics 112
neurological problems, people with
16
neurologists 109
next-of-kin 158, 159, 214
NHS Direct 2, 24–26, 49, 52, 53,
250, 263

NHS Direct Online 24, 27–28, 50
NHS Litigation Authority 243
NHS Low Income Scheme 56, 94, 96–98
NHS Trusts 2–3, 227–230, 244
NICE *see* National Institute for Health and Clinical Excellence
999 calls 24, 30–32
non-English speakers 155, 248–249
non-UK citizens 10, 195–196
nurses
  complaints about 239
  practice 36, 38, 39
  private 46
  *see also* community mental health/psychiatric nurses; district nurses; health visitors
nursing homes
  nursing care charges 10, 180–183, 187
  private 183
  *see also* care homes

occupational therapists (OTs) 34, 80–83, 87, 89, 99, 105, 241
  private 83–84
ophthalmic opticians/optometrists 63, 64, 237, 241
ophthalmologists 64, 67
opticians 2, 63–64
organ donation 198–203
organs, retention of 217
orthoptists 64
orthotics 134
osteopathy 43
osteoporosis 86, 88
out-of-hours services 24, 28, 44, 52
'outreach' services 114
overseas treatment, NHS 156
overseas visitors 10, 195–196

palliative care 184, 205–206
PALS *see* Patient Advice and Liaison Service
Parkinson's disease 7, 17, 84

Patient Advice and Liaison Service (PALS) 38, 49, 88, 101, 112, 137, 173, 175, 227, 228
Patient Forums 257
Patient Transport Service 31–32, 113, 166, 169, 183
pedicurists 133, 135
Pension Credit 93, 164
Personal Medical Service 35
pets, care of 164–165
pharmacists 24, 29, 148–149, 237, 242
physiotherapists/physiotherapy 41, 44, 80, 86, 87, 89, 99, 101, 184, 241
podiatrists *see* chiropodists
post-mortems 216–217, 245
prescriptions 21, 38, 66, 141–143, 242
  private 145, 147, 148
  professionals who can prescribe 145–146
  repeat 46, 146–147
  when abroad 147–148
Pretty, Diane 8, 209
primary care 34
Primary Care Trusts (PCTs) 2
  complaints about 224, 227–230
  *see also* GPs
privacy 18, 19, 20
private health care 10, 24, 43, 46–47, 155, 156–157, 244–245
  *see also* prescriptions, private
prosthetics 134
psychiatric services, NHS 108–109
psychiatrists 109, 110
psychogeriatricians 109, 110
psychosurgery 122
psychotherapy 106–107

records, health 193, 250–255
referrals 38, 39–42, 152
reflexology 43
refusal of treatment 123–124, 210, 211; *see also* advance decisions

register offices 214
Registered Nursing Care
    Contributions 180–183, 186, 188
Regulations 4, 5, 9–10
rehabilitation services 176, 184
religious issues 161–162, 216
Reminyl 111
residential homes see care homes
respite health care 184
resuscitation policies 207–208, 261
rivastigmine 111

safety standards 19, 20
Samaritans 104–105
schizophrenia 103, 115–118
scooters, powered 101
Scotland: 'welfare attorneys' 129
second opinions, getting 40, 250
secondary care 34
'sectioning' 118–123, 124
sheltered housing 173, 178–180
Shopmobility scheme 101
sight see eyesight
sign language 77
Skipton Fund 242
Social Fund 219, 220
social services 45, 165, 169, 171
    and eye problems 67–68
    Single Assessment Process 15,
        118, 170–171
social workers 39
Special Health Authorities 1, 2
specialist health care support 184
spectacles 21, 61, 62, 63, 66, 94–95
speech and language therapists 80,
    84–85, 89, 241
    textphones/textphone enquiries
        26, 77
stoma care 184
Strategic Health Authorities 1, 2, 206

stroke services 16, 84, 85, 90–91
suicidal feelings 104–105
suicide, assisted 209–210
support stockings 21, 92
surgeries see GPs

taxis 69, 96
temporary residents 28, 37, 190
therapies/therapists 79–86, 241
Time Bank UK initiatives 108
tinnitus 76
tissue donation 198–201
tissues, retention of 217
toenail cutting 135, 138–139
transplants see organ donation;
    tissue donation
transport 2, 31–32, 95–96, 113, 183,
    184
Typetalk 77–78

vaccinations
    flu 16, 20–21
    holiday/travel 43
    pneumonia 21
vascular dementia 110; see also
    dementia
visual impairment see eyesight, loss of
vitamin deficiencies 110
volunteers viii, 108, 260–261

Walk-In Centres, NHS 2, 24, 28
walking frames and sticks 82, 101
walking groups 108, 143
'wandering' 112
wart removal 38
wheelchairs 92, 100–101
wigs 21, 92, 95
Women's Royal Voluntary Service
    260–261